MATTHEW FONTAINE MAURY
& JOSEPH HENRY

Also by Patricia Jahns

THE FRONTIER WORLD OF DOC HOLLIDAY

MATTHEW FONTAINE MAURY

&

JOSEPH HENRY

SCIENTISTS

OF THE

CIVIL WAR

By Patricia Jahns

HASTINGS HOUSE · PUBLISHERS

NEW YORK 22

Contents

vi

Introduction and Acknowledgments

In the Mall in Washington, D.C. there is only one statue. It is of Joseph Henry, his bronze eyes fixed watchfully on the front door of the Smithsonian Institution, his back turned on the distractions of the world. He made the Smithsonian his monument. He effaced himself that it might be great and, by so being, help mankind through science. He found it only a name and a sum of money that no one knew what to do with. He gave up his life of invention, his quiet life at Princeton, the sense of security in small, and entered the maelstrom of political life in Washington, at a time when all the currents were irrevocably leading to hatred, viciousness, war.

Of the people who stood in Joseph Henry's way, who tried to keep him small in the world's eyes, the most important was another scientist, the best-known of his day. This man was Matthew Fontaine Maury, the first scientist of the United States Navy, the founder of the science of oceanography.

Matthew Fontaine Maury cannot be compared with anyone, because he opened a new field to investigation; he was the father of all the sciences of the ocean. And he knew it. He gloried in it. He thought it was childish to pretend to modesty when he was constantly being awarded gold medals or diamond-studded ones, or silver services, testimonial dinners or other marks of distinction. He just might have been right: it might have been hypocritical to deny his own worth, but it might have made him more popular with other scientists. And it certainly didn't make him popular with the United States Navy, which then, as now, thought the man who won the battles was the only one that mattered. He, who had helped it to such advantage, was more often its victim than its beneficiary.

But one thing can be said for Maury: he didn't know what the word "quit" meant. When the high brass in the Navy slapped him down, and all those who despised him cheered, he came right back, and came fighting. When he was crippled in an accident he didn't give up. He wrung out of a reluctant world some appreciation of what he had to offer, first a little, then more and more, until he was the public's darling.

And he threw it all away—every last particle—to follow an

viii

ideal that was to ruin his life. He lived to see himself cursed as a traitor and his great inventions denounced as worthless. He went a little bit "off" in the head, shocked by all the virulence directed at him, but still he never quit.

During the same time Joseph Henry was the North's greatest scientist. Firm to his vows of not inventing anything to glorify himself while he worked for the government, he sorted out all the inventions of others, his great mind separating fraud from worth, and channeling it to usefulness for the Union, or gracefully out the back door. Even in the small things, such as bolstering Lincoln in sad times of domestic grief, when the spiritualists were rapping out messages from his dead son and his wife seemed demented, Joseph Henry was there to uncover the fraud.

For the South Maury began to invent "infernal machines" that drowned men while they slept, and many a bad night it gave him, too. This was a "first" that was hardly to be boasted of. He boasted instead, of his sons in the Confederate Army. Robert E. Lee was his friend. Unfortunately, Maury himself was in the Confederate Navy. If one wants to count Jefferson Davis as commander in chief of that Navy, one can work down and down into the command before one finds a single friend of Maury. And they made his life a hell. It seemed sometimes that, between Yankee and Rebel, someone might get his hide after all. At last he had to leave the South and go to England, where, if he got the Confederate naval brass off his neck, he brought down even worse recriminations on his head from the Yankees. He became one of those who arranged for the launching of the Confederate raiders that changed the United States from a major merchant shipping power into a cipher. He was promised short shrift at the end of a rope, considered as much a "pirate" as the sea-going commanders of the Rebel raiders who were engaged in wiping Yankee shipping off the map. Maury, who once had made the oceans safer for man. . . .

Peace brought no end to their work, bringing to Joseph Henry a golden time and to Maury more sufferings than he knew how to handle. But both of these men could say on the day he died, "The world is a better place because I lived in it."

Introduction and Acknowledgments

And we have managed to forget these men.

A generation centered on the acquirement of riches allowed Joseph Henry's name to fade away. The scientist who didn't get rich was a crackpot, the inventor who did was a public benefactor. It was uncomfortable to think about Joseph Henry and his life of self-denial—so we stopped. We put him out of our minds, out of our textbooks, out of the American way of life. Matthew Fontaine Maury was a traitor to one group, a patriot to another. The side that branded him a traitor won, but it would be untrue to say he did not accomplish great things for mankind.

These were great men, great Americans. And I am here to prove it.

Just by chance, I grew up where these men's lives crossed, and by equal chance, came to notice them both where others did not. This was in Arlington, the Virginia suburb of Washington, D.C. In school we studied the Virginia catalog of saints: Spotswood, Washington, Wilson, Lee, Byrd—and Maury. We were taught that Matthew Fontaine Maury was the Pathfinder of the Seas, and while I'm sure I never knew exactly what that meant, I did know I'd better associate the two come exam time. And I was surprised later, in that larger world beyond the South, to find no one had ever heard of this Pathfinder of the Seas. I became his champion (ah, well; aren't we all drawn to the underdog!). Unraveling his story became a hobby over the years, a source of the greatest interest. Little by little I was disillusioned in the hero Maury. In the fascinating person, in the scientist, never. As for Joseph Henry, as you will see later, his child-in-wishes, the Smithsonian Institution, was my refuge throughout a stormy childhood. As I went in the door I could feel his eyes on my shoulder blades, sternly directing at me a look which said, "You behave yourself," and so I was better there than I ever was at home. And Joseph Henry became a kind of watcher-over me in my mind, and later was all the hero that the more colorful Maury had failed at being. When I understood that they were enemies it seemed right, although I could not take sides. I knew myself with Joseph

Henry's friend W. W. Corcoran: I could not fight against the Union, I could not fight against Virginia. And, like him, I ran away. And far away, in another environment, I found perspective.

Where thanks for help are due let the chips fall where they may.

At that happy bureaucracy, the Library of Congress, I will compliment them on the increased efficiency with which the books one asks for are provided. The ratio of success in ordering books used to be about twenty ordered for three received, Now you get the book you want. This is much appreciated. Also, the Local History room is in excellent shape. Other places you are liable to get your information despite them, patiently, or with appeals to your congressman, which I am not above when balked. *Note:* the Maury letters and other papers on Maury that I read in the Manuscript Room were scattered all over with tiny pencilled cross-marks, as were quite a few of the books on Maury. I put a curse on the person(s) that did it.

The Department of Archives provided all requested material by mail with efficiency, courtesy, and dispatch. Which is good, since those elevators in the search section have my number.

I am much indebted to the kind ladies who staff the Genealogical Library of the Mormon Temple in Mesa, Arizona, for their kind permission to use their microfilm reading machines. Also for much valuable assistance in locating descriptions of Yankee areas where I have never been, but where my ancestors' names occurred with unsettling frequency.

I must thank John F. Jameson, archivist at the Smithsonian Institution, for his help with the Henry papers, and the present secretary, sixth since Joseph Henry, Dr. Leonard Carmichael, who kindly gave me permission to quote from the Civil War diary kept by Mary Henry, printed here for the first time.

The Abraham Lincoln Book Shop in Chicago and Queens Books, Long Island City, were of great help in supplying books by mail. The Capitol Hill Book Shop in Washington was also helpful. The Scottsdale Public Library and the Maricopa County Free Library were invariably helpful and pleasant, even when I lost *The World of Washington Irving.*

My aunt, Miss Helen Jahns, of Arlington, was also of great assistance.

For my view of the Civil War I depended largely on my micro-filmed copies of the Washington *Star* for the Civil War decade, 1854–66. All dates and battles were checked in histories and chronologies, but in so large a field there are bound to be mistakes, for which I here humbly beg pardon. The background of the war era is also from the *Star,* and from Mary Henry's diary and the Maury and Henry papers, the former at the Library of Congress, the latter at the Smithsonian Institution, and from the National Park Service. I have about half of the *Century* magazines of the eighties which carried the articles later incorporated into *Battles and Leaders of the Civil War,* and about fifty old *Harper's New Monthly Magazine,* scattered from 1857 to the early eighties, some *Frank Leslie's Illustrated Weekly,* some *Harper's Weekly,* and a precious six months of *The Scientific American* when it was a weekly newspaper during the Civil War. Needless to say, they were invaluable assets. And of course I read everything on the Civil War until I had battle fatigue. And when I disagreed with "Charley Weaver" over the pronunciation of "Minié," I realized that my version (correct but not commonly used) came from almost forgotten *Roses and Drums,* the marvelously accurate radio drama that refought the Civil War for us long ago. It seemed to me that I had always known how to pronounce it, swingingly, "Mini-*ay*-ball," like that. And I'm not that old. It only feels that way.

I was sad to leave these people. When I write a biography the people live for me, and when it ends, they die again. And not just the main characters, but Will Henry, Rutson and Matsy Maury, and "Little Dab" as well. If they live for you they are happy to be remembered. And I have not failed.

Patricia Jahns

Scottsdale, Arizona, 1961.

MATTHEW FONTAINE MAURY
& JOSEPH HENRY

CHAPTER ONE

A Deplorable Situation

IN THAT hot-tempered decade which preceded the Civil War, there were in the United States only two national institutions dedicated to science. Both were in the city of Washington: the United States Naval Observatory and the Smithsonian Institution. The copper-covered dome of the Observatory stood on a low hill near the mud flats along the Potomac River at Twenty-third Street. The redstone towers of the Smithsonian arose in the Mall where Tenth Street crossed the town ditch. Directing them were the two most famous American scientists of their day: little, handsome, limping Matthew Fontaine Maury at the Observatory; and tall, blond, handsome Joseph Henry at the Smithsonian.

They hated each other.

Science just as the pure item was regarded with friendly contempt at this time. The man respected and admired in the eyes of the public—the one little boys wanted to grow up like—was the rich and successful inventor. Professor Henry had invented the useful electromagnet, the first telegraph, and

3

the electric relay; had established the principle of magneto-
electric induction, discovered self-induction, and many other
matters upon which our electronic civilization is based. But
Henry took out no patents, carried none of his discoveries
into marketable form, gave everything freely and openly to
his fellows. He was held in great regard by other American
scientists as the only man in his field who was both successful
and altruistic. Lieutenant Matthew Fontaine Maury, U.S.N.,
had charted the first sea lanes, showed how winds and currents
retarded or helped the routes of both sail- and steam-powered
ships, and gathered together the many scattered facets of
the ocean's ways. He was the first oceanographer; his discoveries made many merchants and shipowners rich, and he
himself profited from the sale of books he wrote on the ocean
for the general public. And he had the great personal satisfaction of knowing himself appreciated. Foreign governments
were continually presenting him with gold medals, he had a
handsomely engraved silver tea service given him by a group
of New York merchants and marine insurance companies,
and an impressive list of honorary degrees. The United States
government seemed to think his monthly pay check was all
the recognition he deserved.

These two, who could only express contempt for each
other—Maury called Henry a "closet scientist" and Henry
said Maury was not ethical—were caught up in the turmoil
that was to end in the Civil War. Washington was a town of
furiously enthusiastic, if not fanatic, cliques; one either was
regarded as being an abolitionist or a secessionist and sometimes such status did not accord with one's actual wish. For
instance, Joseph Henry, a New Yorker and a loyal Unionist,
was very close to Senator Jefferson Davis of Mississippi.
Interestingly, when Davis had been Secretary of War during
Franklin Pierce's administration he had shelved Henry's
suggestion that the Army make a stockpile of gunpowder

components so that in case of war the country would not be dependent on England for its supply; this was to have serious results, as we shall see. Another of Henry's "secesh" friends was W. W. Corcoran, the Washington millionaire and art collector, who fled to England rather than support the Union. Chief Justice Taney, author of the Dred Scott decision, was one of his friends and advisors. Senator John Bell of Tennessee and his wife were frequent house guests at the Smithsonian. The result was that the pro-abolitionists looked down on the Henrys as secesh sympathizers.

Maury, loyal to the South, was in an even stranger position. His admirers, and those who supported him in many a conflict, were primarily the Yankee shipping interests that he had made rich. Unfortunately he also had made for himself many enemies among the secessionists, not the least of whom was that same Jefferson Davis who had been on good terms with Henry, and others who were important politically in the southern faction. Upon this, a matter of siding politically with his personal enemies, Maury was to see his career wrecked.

Washington was atingle with the uneasy approach of war, portents of it popping forth like bubbles in boiling lava. Washington hostesses who had once worried about the table arrangements and how the cake would turn out now found themselves trying to cope with dizzying restrictions on their guest lists. Partygoers became so violent discussing who should be in charge of the Weather Bureau, about the southern demands that we annex Cuba, abolition, the Native American party, that uncouth Lincoln, and other matters, that no one could have any fun. Reticence was thrown to the winds, all semblance of either manners or kindness. Both sides were so powerful in Washington, so arrogant, so sure of success, that their adherents, even those employed by the government, freely named each other traitor and called upon the Constitution to back them up. Everyone was so intensely involved, so bitter, that no one seemed aware of the actual drift of the times.

Of course it didn't take much to make a stir in Washington now. This was the countrified capital, with a population of about seventy-five thousand, where hogs wallowed in mudholes under the shade trees along Pennsylvania Avenue; where runaway slaves were advertised alongside strayed or stolen cows; where the Marine Corps band played concerts attended by the President summer afternoons on the greensward of Capitol Hill. For a jolly outing ladies and gentlemen would sit in their carriages while the young people lolled in the grass to watch a baseball game in the meadow between the White House and the canal with the score—typically, alas—Baltimore, 40, Washington, 24. The most imposing building in town was the white-marble Patent Office, in Greek Classic style, which covered two blocks in the heart of downtown Washington, with, across F Street from it, the Greek-columned marble Post Office. The Treasury Building, around which Pennsylvania Avenue makes a jog at Fifteenth Street, was also a model of the Greek Revival, but of granite. The Capitol, while magnificent on its gentle incline, didn't quite count because it was constantly under construction or reconstruction and was now minus its old dome and awaiting a new one. Washington Monument, at the west end of the Mall, was in the process of a slow and much-halted building program and was, in its backwardness, generally ignored by everyone. The gardens, particularly the vegetable gardens, were the most noted feature around the plain-faced White House.

All these simple, classical white buildings were made to look more grand by the prevailing Washington architecture, low two- or three-story buildings of frame or red brick, with here and there one of stone to note for its material or octagonal shape, but none for its size. The big hotels, such as Willard's and the National, likewise squat, were spread out into a hodge-podge of adjoining buildings. The Central Market, the smaller Northern Liberties Market, and the District buildings were the only other important structures in town. All was so quiet: the tree-lined, unpaved streets; the wide, negleted Mall stretching from the Capitol west to the river with only the tall-towered red Smithsonian and the white stump of Washington Monument in its two-mile length; the air of laziness and indifference; the overpowering stink of the town ditch or "canal" (where Constitution Avenue is now), and the tough "back" parts of town such as Swampoodle or Marble Alley that exploded periodically but, luckily, briefly and locally. Across the Potomac, almost directly in line with the Capitol and Washington Monument, stood the Lee-Custis house on the heights of Arlington, its tall, white-columned porch overlooking the wide expanse of river and the flat little town.

The Smithsonian in its tree-shaded park in the heart of the Mall, reached by crossing a rickety wooden bridge over the canal, was a favorite spot to show off to visitors. As it was then, it is startling looking even today, a place easy to remember. Its design is as if someone had picked up models of the Abbaye-aux-Dames and the Abbaye-aux-Hommes in Caen and dropped them on the floor, and then set a blindfolded person to assemble one building from them, with part of St. Trophîme in Arles sneaked in as a trick. The result came out very long and betowered, the rear of the Abbaye-aux-Hommes and the front of the Abbaye-aux-Dames and the cloisters from St. Trophîme all facing the startled beholder. Inside there were a lecture room, art gallery, a small museum, a library, laboratories, and offices.

It was a pleasant carriage ride out to the red-brick Observatory beside the river, looking in Maury's time much as later pictured, except that the extension to the right-hand

wing was not then built, nor the low dome in the rear. Over
the door was a marker: *Founded* A.D. *1842. John Tyler,
President of the U.S. Abel Upshur, Secretary of the Navy.*
There were four rooms on each floor in the main part and
over them was the copper-sheathed dome, twenty-three feet
across, which revolved on cannon balls rolling in the groove of
a cast-iron rail. Here in the dome was located the 9.6-inch
achromatic refractor, made by Mertz and Mahler in Munich,
the Navy's best telescope. In the west wing was the prime
vertical transit, 4.9 inches, and in the east wing the mural
circle with a 4.1-inch telescope. A comet seeker with a 3.9-inch
glass was kept in the equatorial room. This office was also the
home of the Depot of Charts and Instruments, and while the
telescopes were all very fine to show to sight-seers, Maury's
interest was in, and his fame rested on, charts and the ocean
and sailing. The observers, as a result, were as often to be
found looking into oceanographic matters as astronomical
ones.

The men in charge of these government agencies, Joseph
Henry and Matthew Fontaine Maury, knew themselves great
men in their own day, scientists of a wider implication than
Louis Agassiz, the zoologist, or Asa Gray, the botanist; Amos
Eaton, the geologist, or Benjamin Silliman, the chemist—
all of whom were and should still be famous American scientists. Henry might be compared to Benjamin Franklin,
Maury to that Benjamin Thompson who is known in Europe
as Count Rumford. Henry's name was forgotten because his
self-effacing personality buried itself in the Smithsonian,
while making the Smithsonian the great gathering-place for
knowledge which it has been for more than a hundred years.
Only in the technical aspects of the electronic age is his name
immortalized: the henry—the international unit for measuring electrical induction—is named for him, as the volt was
named for Volta, the ampere for Ampere, the farad for Fara-

8

day. Maury's fame was lost, ironically enough, because for once in his life he cast aside materialistic considerations, just once gave into idealism and nobleness of purpose. He gave his loyalty to his home in Virginia out of pure sentimental attachment when the Civil War came along, instead of cleaving to that commercial Yankeedom he had helped put where it was. But with the passing of the years, as the ocean came to be realized as the last earthly frontier, the vanquished oceanographer's work was rediscovered and his intent, at least, appreciated. There is charm in that old book of his; the opening lines seem to carry you away:

There is a river in the ocean. In the severest droughts it never fails, and in the mightiest floods it never overflows. Its banks and its bottoms are of cold water, while its current is of warm. The Gulf of Mexico is its fountain and its mouth is in the Arctic Seas. It is the Gulf Stream. There is in the world no other such majestic flow of waters. . . .

CHAPTER TWO

Young Mat Maury
of Tennessee

TUESDAY, JANUARY 14, 1806, on a 400-acre farm near
Fredericksburg, Virginia, the seventh of nine children was
born to Richard and Diana Minor Maury. In accordance
with first-family-of-Virginia tradition he was named after
distinguished ancestors and rich living relatives: Matthew
Fontaine Maury. His father's forebears had been Huguenot
refugees long settled in Virginia; his mother's paternal ancestors were the Doodes, a Dutch family that had taken the
name Minor and whose members had married into old families
of English descent, the Carrs, the Dabneys, the Cosbys.
The farm, which they partly owned and partly leased, had
been owned originally by Governor Spotswood and they had
gotten it on August 31, 1797 (with legal papers witnessed
by more than a dozen people) from Henry Lee, Esquire,
and Ann his wife, of Stratford Hall in Westmoreland
County.[1]

11

In nearby Fredericksburg, ghosts of Revolutionary glory had as yet to be eclipsed by new names and bloody battles of internecine war. Proudly rising on a hillside, each side street the usual block higher than the one below it, Fredericksburg stood over the tall masts of coast-trade schooners that thronged her wharfs. Here was the head of navigation on the Rappahannock, a lively place for shipping north the grain crops and tobacco grown in the rich Tidewater, and importing fine wines, groceries, furniture, silver, and yard goods. Caroline and William streets saw great wagon trains lumbering in continually, warehouses along the river bulged with wealth, and bigger and bigger houses were built on Princess Anne Street on up the hill. Richard Maury's brother Fontaine was a wealthy trader and landowner and his wife's brothers were lawyers in this thriving inland port.

Despite the distinguished connections, the new baby's branch of the Maury family seems to have been far from sophisticated. Richard, his father, was remembered principally for the volume and carrying quality of his voice; he could be heard yelling at his slaves from a mile away. Diana, his mother, appears to have been thoroughly dominated by her strong-minded husband. Their farm was a few miles west of Fredericksburg, not in the Tidewater, but on the edge of the Wilderness where nothing grew well but scrub pines, skinny oaks, and thick-matting undergrowth. The land had been worn out by overplanting tobacco, and the Maurys lacked the financial assets that, invested in it, would have brought it back.

To complicate Richard Maury's troubles, the British were beginning that series of hostile and arrogant acts which, coupled with their refusal to treat their late colonies as being worthy of respect, ended in the War of 1812. Indignation over the seizure of our shipping and the impressment of our seamen seethed in the South and West. To the people of those

12

sections, it was an insult pure and simple, and small Mat and his older brother John Minor got an unnecessary earful of pride and bragging not quite intended as they took it. In the North the loss of seamen and cargoes was more cheerfully borne because they were making so much money from those that escaped. France and England were at war, and the Yankees were getting rich because of it.

Then the British frigate *Leopard* stopped the *Constitution* off Hampton Roads and impressed four of her sailors as British deserters, took them off to Halifax, and hanged two of them. Our nation's formal protest to the British government was not only ignored but the British navy was given well-publicized orders to be even stricter than they had been before in impressing seamen for their cruelly-treated crews.

What an outburst of indignation was heard in the South now! And along the frontier, where they remembered British-instigated Indian massacres, and where they wanted the Indians' land to expand in!

John Minor Maury, eldest son of Richard and Diana Maury, but still only thirteen years old, joined the United States Navy as a midshipman. This was in 1809. In that same year there was a depression in the agricultural South owing to Jefferson's embargo against trading with the warring nations. Richard Maury began to think about the grass being greener on the other side of the fence. His older brother Abraham had gone to Tennessee a few years before and made good. Why shouldn't he do the same?

Richard Maury was a sternly religious man, having left the religion of his father, that Reverend James Maury against whom Patrick Henry had pleaded in the Parson's Cause. He *would* kick against the pricks. Because of the depression and generally disturbed conditions following, it took him almost a year to get ready to move to Tennessee, but in August of 1810 Nathanial Gordon of Fredericksburg gave Richard

13

three hundred dollars in Federal money for his one hundred acres.[2] The rest of the land reverted to the Lees, and the Maurys were off.

Mat, with his curly red-brown hair, big blue eyes, and engaging grin, was not quite five years old. He had a chunky, sawed-off physique, a kind of stubby look, as if he might not grow very tall, but he was sturdy and healthy. Already, part exaggerated, part mere shadow, one could see the shape of a personality to come, spoiled, proud, given to useless and wholeheartedly enjoyed tantrums, very intelligent, and so charming in manner and appearance that it was difficult really to know him. Part of his pride expressed itself in lifelong devotion to his family. His excess of hysterical outbursts no doubt was owing, in part anyway, to his father's incessant bullying. John Minor had gotten away from this mistreatment, its harshness backed up by the parental interpretation of biblical precept, and his other brothers and sisters seemed cowed by it, but Mat stood his ground and fought back.

The Maurys had to walk West. His older sister Matilda carried Mat as she trudged down the dusty, rut-corrugated road beside the tall wagon such as the ones the traders used, and which now held everything his family owned.

In 1810 the Conestoga wagon was the pioneers' chief means of transporting their goods; it held a lot, it held together, and it was maneuverable. It was sixteen feet long, with rear wheels six feet high and the tops of the hoops eleven feet off the ground, all spread with a twenty-four-foot canvas, dusty and dingy above the high sides and front of the brightly-painted wagon body. Only the driver rode, on a seat well below the top of the body, like a bracket nailed on the front, as the wagon jarred and jolted its springless way along an ungraded wilderness trail.

The Wilderness Road, from Virginia through the Cumberland Gap, had been opened to wagon traffic in 1795 and

carried almost all the overland freight that moved in and
out of Kentucky and Tennessee. The Indians were still about
and while they seemed disposed to be peaceable, no one quite
trusted them and the government was being asked to move
them to the Far West. Mat's Uncle Abraham, a former colonel in the Revolutionary army, had moved to Tennessee as
soon as the land there had been opened up for public sale
at two dollars an acre (half cash on purchase, the balance
in four years), and knew the ropes and could help them.

All along the way, down the Valley Pike to pick up the
Wilderness Road (later Boone's Trace), then the hundred-
mile struggle through the mountains at Cumberland Gap,
then along the old Warrior's Path the Indians had worn
deep by following the line of least resistance, turning off to
the Knoxville Road, and at last to the Old Walton Road
that led to Nashville, they saw a great busyness, a migration
that told them they were part of the pulse of the times. Each
depression turned the people's eyes West, fostering a new
surge of expansion.

Traders might not carry much out yet but furs, hides,
corn, cotton, and tobacco, and these not plentifully during
this depression period, but salt, gunpowder, lead, and house-
wares of tin and heavy crockery were swapped for when the
long, bell-laden Conestoga trains came rumbling and rattling
into the growing clearings of the frontier. The West-travel-
ing family stopped at the wayside wagon yards like everyone else using the punishing road; the older children were
admonished to keep the little ones out of the hog-feeding
troughs, and for less than a dollar they shared a common
meal, a common roof, and any dances, brawls, cuttings,
bottle-throwings, and lie-swappings that they couldn't get
out of, and were up at 3:00 A.M. to get ready for the road.
Then raw torches burned to light the confusion: the freighters in their high boots and wide-brimmed hats, bearded and

foul-mouthed, hitching up their teams decorated with furs and hung with gay fringes and bells as big as dinner plates, each turning out his sixty feet of team and wagon in as grand a style as possible, determined to be the bully boy of the wagon train. And the stagecoaches, bright-painted and cheerless, rattling away in grand fashion toward the first upset of the day, all the chilled passengers looking sleepy, angry, and apprehensive. Then the herders with their cattle, hogs, and horses, dull fellows compared to the stage drivers and freighters, not yet come into their own as best of all, the cowboys. And at last, the forlorn, stubborn Maurys and their lone wagon, their kids, slaves, dogs, horses, going West.

If there were no Indians to fight there were Indians to be afraid of, wild rivers to ford, steep and sharp-curved mountain trails to struggle along, illnesses, storms to keep them holed up in stinking taverns, dust to choke and cloak them, rough people and the silence of the virgin forest to alarm them equally, and thrust everywhere they went the ugliness, the stump-field, shack-building, rag-tail ugliness of the frontier. But if the Maurys had come from better, if there were books instead of whisky in their barrels, that made no difference. They survived looking at the frontier; they became dedicated to its way of life.

Near the crossroads community of Franklin, which took its name from the first state name for Tennessee, the Maurys bought their land, cleared their fields, put up their hickory-rail and cedar-shingle cabin, dug their well, built barn, slave quarters, and necessary house, grew their crops, and helped and were helped by their pioneer neighbors. This is that rolling country by the Harpeth River south of Nashville, good farm land, not too far from markets, and in a progressive area where the necessities of civilization were soon built: churches, courthouse, roads, schools. But all of it

16

lacking the polish and prettiness that come with age and planning. This was the West in 1811.

Mat's first home to remember was this one-room cabin with its floor of halved logs neatly trimmed, one wall all fireplace (it heated, cooked, let in fresh air, and was often their light by night), their precious furniture set about self-consciously, and the loft above for the children to sleep in.

If one liked the outdoors, there was plenty to do, once away from the strict father and his ideas of what something to do consisted of. Mat and his elder brother Richard lived in a half-wilderness area, still rich with wild animals, if not enough to trap for a living, certainly enough to keep two small boys busy, and the Harpeth was not only fishable but swimable. There were large stands of the once-great hardwood forest in which to play robber barons and Indians and pirates and to hide oneself and enjoy the secret treasures of boyhood. Along the roads, edging the fields and woods, were wild primroses, geraniums, Queen Anne's lace, and gentians, carried home crushed in dirty little hands, for Mother to sigh over, pausing for a moment in her work to tell them again about the scented, formal boxwood gardens of Virginia, and the adventures of the infinitely superior people who lived there, rich, assured, mannered. People to be proud of.

But life around their father, even with slaves, was mostly work. He believed that sparing the rod spoiled the child and he was determined to do right by his and to bring them up in the fear of the Lord, so they would jump when told to jump. Life was mostly draw the water, feed the chickens, milk the cows, slop the hogs, plant the cotton, hitch up the team, hoe the corn, sharpen the ax, turn out the sheep, pick the beans, take a hand with the churn, chop the wood, give a hand with the clothes boiler, memorize your Bible lesson, pick up kindling, to a loud voice, criticizing.

Mat was being brought up in a way that, to one of his romantic, luxury-loving, impatient nature, was intolerable. He burned with fires of ambition and rebellion and his father rode him whip and tongue, determined to beat the foolishness out of him. Mat associated himself with the Virginians of the family; too proud to be molded into someone's puppet, his refuge was violent, completely undisciplined rages. As he got older he learned to restrict himself to words in these emotional outbursts, but he never learned to do without gusts of passion at everything that balked him. His father was as determined as Mat was and the two were constantly at odds. Of course Mat's father always won. He could quote the Bible to answer on all accounts and there was no comeback in this strict Presbyterian household to "The Bible says so."

Mat had an example and an inspiration of how to escape always in his mind: the brother who was now in the Navy, John Minor. No matter how his father might shout at him or bully him, there were adventures awaiting him far from the drudgery of the farm. Kicking barefooted along the dusty road on his way to a one-room school, past the stumpy fields with their brush fences, the little cabins with their shed outposts and unkempt yards, and the woods still clinging close, full of tangles and undergrowth, Mat would dream of John Minor's adventures in the beautiful, romantic, rich islands of the South Seas.

There having been a lull in the war furor, John Minor had obtained a furlough to join the crew of a merchant ship bound for China. Skipper of the ship was another United States Navy officer on furlough, Captain William Lewis, who appointed John Minor his lieutenant. After an uneventful voyage they reached Nukahiva Island in the Marquesas.

Nukahiva seemed a model South Seas paradise. No flat coral atoll, it had mountains and waterfalls and green luxuriant growth and sunny glens full of breadfruit groves and wide sandy beaches lined with palms and friendly natives and dangerous cannibals (interchangeable in person, as it turned out). Here John Minor and six seamen were left to gather sandalwood while Captain William Lewis and the rest sailed on to China. They were supposed to make one of those flying stops for which the American ships were famous, and head straight back to Nukahiva. But the War of 1812 finally got started formally and their ship was blockaded in port by British men-of-war.

Marooned on a cannibal island, John Minor and his sailors found themselves pawns in an intertribal war. Herman Melville wrote of just such experiences on this very island, where later he jumped ship, in his novel *Typee*. Almost unbearably beautiful was this island paradise, its people like forest gods, and death part of the daily ritual. Five of John Minor's sailors were killed and served up as "long pig." Finally, where some coconut palms grew close together, John Minor and the surviving sailor, named Baker, made a nest by lashing a platform together in the treetops. Here they had access to food from the friendlier and more civilized of the two tribes, and a lookout over the ocean for a ship to rescue them. Also a rope ladder to pull up in case of trouble.

Back in Tennessee the Maurys avidly read the weekly paper for news of the war. It was mostly to the bad on the side of the neglected Army, the Tennessee state militia doing better fighting the Creeks, but the brunt of the action fell on the tiny Navy. Fortunately the Navy had not been able to stagnate after the Revolution. There had been an undeclared war at sea with France just before the turn of the century that had made our sea-fighting force very popular with the public, and several new men-of-war had been built. Then the Tripolitan War with the Barbary Corsairs from 1801 to 1805 had kept our navy still busy, although that victory was more of a draw, and only a useless gunboat fleet

19

had been built. Our Navy, trained to the teeth, consisted of eighteen fighting ships of all classes.

The British Navy, also trained to the teeth from years of war with France, consisted of 230 ships of the line and 116 frigates. Fortunately for the United States, England was still at war with France during most of this time. Otherwise we scarcely would have done as well as we did. As it was, we were blockaded quite effectively. Congress issued letters of marque that permitted our now-useless merchant fleet to go a-privateering, and our battleships offered every inducement for the best men to sail on them and won a thunderous number of victories. We ran our edge of luck as thin as it would go.

Out in the Pacific one lone American man-of-war, the light frigate *Essex*, 32 guns, under Captain David "Logan" Porter, was destroying the British whaling fleet and sinking every British merchantman she could catch up with. Hearing from some American whalers in the Galápagos Islands that British warships were about, Porter headed for an out-of-the-way beach where he could careen his ship and clean off her bottom, grown logy with seaweed. Wanting to be sure that his ship and the prizes he had taken would be safe, he sailed all the way to the nearest islands of the South Pacific and put into Comptroller Bay at Nukahiva in October of 1813.

Rescued after almost two years, John Minor Maury promptly took up his commission in the Navy, now as a lieutenant. One of the prize ships had been renamed the *Essex Junior*, and he was made second on her, under Lieutenant John Downes. After they had cleaned off the seaweed, put down a native war, and founded the town (it was really a small fort) of Madisonville, the *Essex* and the *Essex Junior* went back to raiding British shipping along the Pacific coast of South America.

Young Mat Maury of Tennessee

On March 28, 1814, off Valparaiso, Chile, they lost the *Essex* despite all the brave efforts of "Logan" Porter and his crew to the British men-of-war *Cherub* and *Phoebe*. The flag that had been Porter's pride, reading "Free Trade and Seamen's Rights," had gone down with the *Essex's* maintop in a storm just before the battle. All the survivors were loaded on board the *Essex Junior*, which had surrendered when caught alone in Valparaiso Harbor, and started for internment in Canada. On their way, off Long Island while becalmed in a heavy fog, almost all of them escaped ashore in a longboat. Among them were "Logan" Porter, John Minor Maury, and Porter's twelve-year-old foster son, a midshipman from Tennessee named David Farragut.

There was a life to dream about, and young Mat Maury did plenty of dreaming.

The War of 1812 dragged to a close and was ended by a treaty that left the causes of the conflict unresolved. Tennessee felt that it had done itself more than proud with Andy Jackson winning the Battle of New Orleans. And the Navy, feeling understandably invincible, remembered some unfinished business with the Barbary States and went back and cleaned them up. Then it set out to rid the Caribbean of piracy, which kept it busy for quite a while.

Now Tennessee began to expand and prosper, cotton-happy in the rich ante-bellum South. In fact, Tennessee began to be beautiful now that man's hand lay more familiarly on the land. The last of the Cherokees were moved out. Andy Jackson built Hermitage up Nashville way, and in Columbia Sam Polk, father of James K. Polk, had just finished a small, graceful mansion. Other great houses were built, and pleasant small ones. The fields lost their lumpy look, fences that cost money were put up, and more and more land was brought under cultivation. And no longer were Tennesseans nobodies. Andy Jackson started on his way to becoming president. John H. Eaton of Franklin was a member of Congress and would wind up one of the scandal-victimized members of Jackson's "kitchen" cabinet. Davy Crockett was known to everyone: the "coonskin Congressman." It was a coming-up time for Tennessee as it was a falling-away time for Virginia.

But Tennessee was a part of the South. Her economy was felt to be a slave economy. The Maurys and the folks around Franklin thought, like most of the South, that those sneaky Yankees had to be watched, or they would try to run the country (i.e., do away with slavery). They already controlled the House of Representatives because of their larger population. The Senate was controlled by the South and a southern-dominated political party, and they intended to keep on controlling it.

In Franklin, now grown to a prosperous little trading center, was Harpeth Academy (three teachers), where Mat was sent to school following a fall when his back was injured so badly that he was at first expected to be crippled for life. With many short men some accident in their childhood is pointed out with: "He never grew after that." Such was the case with Mat; he was only five feet six inches tall when he was full grown, if he was that tall. But short men seemed to run in the Maury family then: his nephew Dabney was only five feet three, and his youngest son, Matsy, was not much taller. So probably this accident had little to do with how tall he grew—but it changed all his life another way.

Seeing Mat with his tongue almost bitten through, painfully but stubbornly creeping about the house after the accident, his father relented from some of his strict disciplinarian ways and encouraged Mat to study to be a doctor. His teachers at the Academy apparently felt that he was an exceptional scholar. Ignoring his father's request that he study medicine, Mat found that he had a natural gift for

22

languages, an intuitive feel for mathematics, and a desire
to learn, the most important gift of all. Out there, beyond
these low hills and green fields, there were challenges, the
world not understood and indeed not all explored. Someday
—it was always someday and not now. So he drugged himself with study, made every good impression that he could,
and waited.

On June 23, 1824, John Minor Maury died of yellow
fever aboard the store ship *Decoy* and was buried at sea off
Norfolk. He was twenty-eight years old and flag captain of
the pirate-chasing fleet in the West Indies, the youngest
man of his rank in the Navy, the most promising. His whole
life ran before Mat's eyes continually. Not only the South
Seas adventures, but his later daring exploits during the
war with MacDonough of the Lakes when one of our country's really decisive naval victories had been won in New
York State, his marriage to rich Uncle Fontaine's daughter
Eliza back in Fredericksburg, their children, and after the
War of 1812, the long, victorious fight against the pirates
in the West Indies. He had died while carrying an account
of their victory back to the President.[3]

Richard Maury took his eldest son's death very hard. The
Bible came flying out as if on springs and was waved about
and quoted from. It was the doing of the Lord, punishment
for his sins, and he began to supervise his family even more
closely and watch over them so that he might not be hurt
again by one of them.

To Mat, life again grew intolerable. He not only had to
escape all this now, but he saw himself as a replacement for
that other Maury, now dead, to carry on his work, his great
name. He was very bright and this was one of those challenges that he loved, a balk that made the flames of life burn
more brightly while he struggled to overcome it.

Me and Elick are going to the na-na-na-vy; it sounds

23

*large now, don't it? but it is a fact. Mr. Curran has written
to the Hon. John H. Eaton on that subject and besides Mr.
Owen has written for me to his brother George and Samuel
Houston. My Dad and Mom say I shall not go; but you can
guess whether I will or not.* Nineteen years old, he wrote this
to his friend William Ventress, on February 6, 1825.

When his commission came later in the spring there was
commotion all over Williamson County and even into neighboring Maury County. Mat's father meant it when he said
he didn't want him to go. He refused to give him any money
or even to lend him any. And since Mat Maury was not the
kind of person to work for hired-hand wages or go to rail
splitting or whatever he could pick up in a rural community,
he had to scheme for ways and means. He was going, there
was no doubt about that. He went to everyone with his problem, wrote to everyone, and finally managed to scrape together the bare necessities and a horse borrowed from his
uncle Abraham's overseer, with a promise to sell the horse
and send back the money as soon as he got to his rich relatives in Virginia. William Hasbrouck, one of his teachers at
the Academy and a member of the old Huguenot family of
Newburgh, New York, who was to be his steadfast friend all
his life, gave him thirty dollars as a token for helping teach
the younger students. And, although he didn't know this
when he started out, William Ventress had sent two hundred
dollars to him in care of a friend who worked at the Navy
Department in Washington, not wanting to antagonize
Mat's father further by sending it to him at home.

His father refused to say good-by to him.

Young Mat Maury, late in the spring of his nineteenth
year, rode off from a worried mother and a flock of brothers
and sisters, none of them daring to be too riotous, not even
his favorite brother Richard, for fear of the old man. Mat
had a fresh, ruddy, lively look, his irrepressibly curly, dark,

red-tinged hair waving over his collar, his deeply set blue
eyes very serious and reserved as became the responsible
young midshipman, and his face set back toward the east,
toward fame and fortune. Before leaving he'd had a temperamental outburst against his cousin Alexander Maury
("Elick") because he backed out and wouldn't go.⁴ So he
had plenty to think about as he rode away.

NOTES TO CHAPTER TWO

1. *Spotsylvania County Records, 1721–1800*, Crozier.
2. *Ibid.*
3. *Recollections of a Virginian*, D. H. Maury.
4. Letter from Maury to William Ventress, dated November 13, 1825, "U. S. Frigate Brandywine, off Gibralter." He
bitterly regrets his outburst against Elick, but too late: his
cousin never figures in his life again.

(Note: the reference to his father's loud voice is made
many years later, when his father is an old man, living with
Mat in Washington shortly before he died in 1842.)

Joseph's mother had to provide for the family, taking in boarders, asking her well-to-do brother in Schenectady for help, scrimping and mending and doing without. She had one of those cast-iron Presbyterian consciences that were so prevalent in our country at a time when they were sorely needed, and no complaining was allowed. If cold porridge was all there was to eat, grace must be said, and meant, for there being anything to eat at all. It was a fine way to bring up children so they would be full of character and a credit to the community but it wasn't much fun for the child, and in Joseph Henry's case it gave him a lifelong contempt for *things*. Ideas, people, and places he valued. Things, no.

Fortunately Ann was able to make matters a little easier for everyone just by the fact of herself. She might say to Joseph and his little brother, "How can ye be laughing and thinking of nothing but play when ye've immortal souls to save?" which would cast a child either into a fit of the glowering doldrums or the giggles, but a-weel, she was a tiny blond thing and very, very beautiful. They loved her dearly.

Home was a small white frame house on South Pearl Street, which was one of the long streets of the town, running parallel with the river but a way up the steep hill that crowned the town. Albany was still Dutch, full of stone houses set with their stepped gable ends to the street, and despite the steady onrush of progress, Stephen Van Rensselaer was patroon here, with twenty miles square of land all his and rented out to make him look rich. Joseph Henry, for all that he was a Scot, looked right at home, for in addition to having a head as square as any Dutchman, he was blue-eyed and blond and slow to be making up his mind.

Albany had been made the state capital the year he was born, and the sturdy, plain stone building that was the first state capitol building was now being built. North of town great lumber mills were transforming the Adirondack forest

28

cover into planks for houses and ships. There were 131 stores in town, 68 storehouses of goods waiting to go some-place, and they said 500 vehicles climbed State Street hill every day. There were flour mills and a new foundry, and along the busy water front three quays handled the river traffic to New York City, of which 45 sloops were owned by Albany traders. West through the Mohawk and southwest through Cherry Valley ran the toll turnpikes that carried the main stream of new settlers and commercial goods to Lake Erie and all the produce of that vast frontier back again. In the winter, local farmers would bring their goods into Albany on sledges. In the spring, fur trappers, dressed like poor farmers in butternut dyed homespun, but with Indian moccasins on their feet, would come by canoe down the waterway from the Adirondacks with their priceless furs —marten, beaver, otter, mink, fisher, fox—and walk silently down the clean, paved streets in a hurry to forget their hard solitude in the many local taverns. But some stopped to tell General Van Rensselaer that they knew the canoe route to Canada, if they should ever be needed as scouts, because the Little Medicine Mouse had been heard singing in the Far North Woods and the Indians said that meant there would soon be war.

And in the midst of all this prosperity and the coming and going of the great Conestogas and the fights at the Drovers Inn and the constant influx of new faces and the presence of Governor John Jay at the public market in the middle of Broadway and the new businesses always starting and expansion and prosperity on every hand—things went worse with the Henrys instead of better. When Joseph was six years old his father died, and now really serious steps had to be taken: the family was broken up. Joseph was sent to live with his widowed Grandma Alexander and her twin brother in Galway. An uncle took him on the coach that

29

carried them (for sixty-four cents) across the sandy pine
barren by turnpike to Schenectady, then to the little village
of Amsterdam, where one of the mansions built by the Mohawk lover, the Tory William Johnson, still stood, and
thence back north by east through the southern foothills of
the Adirondacks to Galway.

Galway had a general store, a meetinghouse, a church, the
district school, and a handful of houses. Around it, where
the forest had been cleared, were some poor farms. It was
that miserable step behind the frontier, the backwoods. It
was a frontier that had failed. North there were only the
rising ranks of mountains, and, eventually, Canada. From a
hilltop looking south and east one could see the Mohawk
Valley and the vast plain that lies south of Saratoga Spa,
where only last year, in 1802, Gideon Putnam had built a
new hotel, Union Hall, in the hope of acquiring some of the
tourist and health-seeking business so flourishing at Ballston
Spa ten miles away.

The Alexanders were good people, of the proper rigid
Calvinistic cut, but they were not his lovely mother and his
baby brother James back home in busy, lively Albany. A
certain depression seems to have set in about this time in
his personality. He couldn't quite be happy. His sense of
humor wilted. The orphan boy, the charity child, he fancied
people sneered at him for his poverty and a totally imagined
differentness which he couldn't change but which he had
sense enough to be ashamed of. He began to withdraw from
this painful and empty world into the world of dreams.

He was no good on the farm. He was always mooning
around and making the lot of those naturally industrious
a nervous torment. They sent him to Israel Phelps' one-room
country school which served the whole district without crowd-
ing and got no better results. He learned a very little read-

ing and a very little writing and even less arithmetic, and then he and Mr. Phelps declared a truce.

He had never developed a fondness for objects such as those usually so dear to children, a white stone with a hole worn in it, a lead bullet curiously crumpled, a bit of string, normally found cramming boys' pockets. But he had a white rabbit he played with even more than other children would have; and he thought wistfully of holding his own in the discussions that went on in Broderick's store, shining as the loafers' wit, not knowing any better. Music, even the forthright country fiddler tunes, fell on tone-deaf ears; he couldn't tell "How Stands the Glass Around" from "Greensleeves."

Storytelling, the most enjoyable way of passing the time, was mostly of ghosts and clanking chains and cold hands clutching at you in the dark, the legacy of the Old World having been handed on freely by the Dutch settlers. But stories were also told of hair being raised authentically: this was the land of the Mohawks and nearby of other tribes of the Iroquois Nation, and only twenty-five years ago they had taken sides with the British during the Revolution and massacred hereabouts quite freely. Old Nick Stoner, the trapper and Indian killer, was still around; everyone knew him, always wearing his fringed buckskins and calling his women "wife" as coolly as if they really were. And everywhere you went you saw the sturdy stone houses built by William Johnson, the man who loved the Mohawks, and who had turned them like a savage flood against his best friends when they rebelled against his king. Joseph Brant, the Mohawk chief—Bloody Brant, they called him—was really Johnson's half-breed son, everyone said.

When the talk turned to prosaic things, such as the latest news in the Schenectady weekly paper, the *Mohawk Mer-*

cury, about the British insistence on the right of search on the high seas, and the price of grain in Albany, and the work being done to make the Mohawk navigable, Joseph would wander away.

The air was so clear, so truthful and uncharitable here. The very ax marks could be seen on the squared logs with their neatly dovetailed corners on every house. Yet a beautiful Iroquois princess walked before Joseph's eyes far more distinctly than the sight of the chickens enjoying his grandmother's vegetable garden.

At last, in desperation, his grandmother put him out half days to work at Broderick's general store. He was ten years old.

Ten years old, and he never did anything right. It was made a moral issue, this failure of his to toe the mark before everyone's patience was lost; the unco' guid never let him forget it. The natural result was to change him—from slow to make up his mind into unable to make up his mind. When he had to make a decision under pressure he was helpless; the works stalled. He couldn't. Going to work for kind and patient Mr. Broderick was a blessing in disguise for Joseph Henry. Despite his thinness and gawkiness, his habitually sad, dreamy expression, he was good-looking and made a lasting impression on people who met him. Mr. Broderick found him of sufficient use to keep on, and he was encouraged to continue attending half days at Mr. Phelps' school in the hope that some of it might sink in.

And then one day something fine and lucky happened to him. Most of his life had been devoted to making knocks into boosts and he was getting pretty sick of it. Actually, right at the beginning, this looked like another one of those miserable episodes; because his pet rabbit escaped one summer afternoon while he was playing with it and ran away.

Be Kind to the Likes of Joe Henry

Joseph, who really loved what few things he had to love, took off after his pet.

A cottony white tail disappeared under the village meetinghouse. Joseph got down on his hands and knees and found a loose board around the foundation posts. After pulling it farther away he was able to crawl under the building and catch his pet. On his hands and knees, turning to crawl back out, he saw a wide shaft of light overhead. Another loose board, which with understandable curiosity he pulled on, gave him access into a storeroom, after some wriggling and britches tearing. Beside a cobweb-shrouded window, neglected and damp-stained, was a whole bookcase full of romantic novels. Cuddling the rabbit in his arms, he stared at the shabby brown bindings stamped with gold. Hidden away, forgotten by the pious, here was the world. He knew what his grandmother would do if she caught him reading a novel: he'd be lucky to sit down inside a week. Besides, he couldn't read very well, anyway. But temptation triumphed. He curled up on the floor beside the window in his worn-out homespun, and his shoes which had been made with one square toe and one round toe as punishment for not making up his mind right away how he wanted them, with the rabbit in his lap, and started to spell his way through *A Fool of Quality*, by Sir Philip Brooke.[2]

Alas for the forces of evil that abound in the world! *A Fool of Quality* is so pious and so heaped with ☞ MORAL ☜ that it could only have benefited our naughty sneaker-in and surreptitious reader of forbidden fiction. And besides, the story was so intriguing, the wicked brother so vile and the good brother so saintly, that he couldn't wait to see what would happen next. He came again and again, careful that no one saw him, and the first thing he knew he was reading with ease.

33

Mr. Broderick, of course, soon found out about it and was able to borrow the books for Joseph to read without his having to keep on breaking and entering. He even let Joseph read books of his own, poetry as well as prose, and the boy was launched on the literary bender that lasted all his life. But about the time that he had memorized every book he could without his grandmother's finding out about it, he had to leave.

The War of 1812 had started and people living on the New York frontier looked uneasily toward the weakly-defended Canadian border, remembering the Indian raids on isolated settlements of the last war. Having lost a husband, Joseph's mother was of no mind to lose a son, too. She sent for Joseph to come back to Albany at once.

Joseph had visited his mother several times, and knew that Albany was still expanding and might have as many as six or seven thousand people by now, but he was surprised at the changes war had brought. Ships were crowded so closely along the wharfs extending out into the river that their rigging tangled blackly against the sky, the town was full of soldiers and, oddly enough, sailors, on their way to defend the forts and lakes to the north. New York state militia paraded smartly on the square, eying the townspeople patronizingly because they were enlisted to fight on the soil of their native state only so all New Yorkers could feel sure that they would always have an army. Material to build ships on the lakes moved through town, west to Lake Erie and north to Lake Champlain. Grain to feed everyone's armies poured into Albany. There was plenty left to feed the Canadian armies of King George, too, so they did. After all, they were used to trading with Canada and nobody felt that the people far away in Washington had too much control over the country. There was secession talk in New England.

Apprenticed to a watchmaker and silversmith, John Doty,

Joseph watched the bustle in town and read the war news in the daily paper as avidly as anyone. The Fort Dearborn massacre put everyone on edge, all along the frontier, and the defeats at Niagara and Montreal—largely caused by the refusal of the New York state militia to set foot out of their state—showed the need for a regular army, well trained and with a leadership potential to take over when the top lads with pull and influence got them into trouble. Some victories on the high seas put a better face on things soon, however. But now the British had blockaded the southern seacoast and soon spread to Long Island with their fleet of warships. The Yankees in New England, while still making loud secession noises, were building swift ships for the privateering business as fast as they could.

Watchmaking was most distasteful to Joseph; it was like being buried alive in a transparent tomb overlooking a world full of gaiety and laughter. Life for him just refused to be anything like it was in the books. But he stuck at it until he was a fair mechanic, and it was to be of the greatest use to him later on, this hard-learned dexterity with fine wires and tools.

The British burned Buffalo, then Lewiston, and the country all around was pillaged by the Indians; an act forbidding trading with the enemy was passed and then had to be repealed because where it could be enforced whole towns almost starved and where it couldn't the trade went on anyway. And then Napoleon quit his fight against the British and the latter began sending their crack Continental-trained troops over here. But we won at Chippewa and fought to a draw at Lundy's Lane and then abandoned Fort Erie. Captain Perry had won his sea battle on Lake Erie, and now, in this early fall of 1814, they were getting ready to fight on Lake Champlain.

John Minor Maury was one of Captain Thomas Mac-

35

Donough's officers, and very likely Joseph Henry saw the Virginian in Albany busy with affairs about the ships being built by Adam and Noah Brown up on the lake. Surely he was one who cheered MacDonough's victory, which left the British with no recourse but to fall back to Canada, abandoning most of their supplies.

After the disastrous burning of Washington and our subsequent successful defense of Baltimore, the British Army sailed for Jamaica where they refitted for the attack on New Orleans. Then the war was soon over, but it would be a hundred years before we were friendly with the British.

In late 1813 John Doty had gone out of business and moved West with the new stream of hard-luck Yankees who had gone broke during the embargo and blockade. Joseph had not been sorry to be free from his apprenticeship, especially since Mr. Doty had told him bluntly he was too dull to learn. The Henrys had a family conclave on what to do with Joseph. There was no thought of his going back to Galway. He seemed to lack the physical skills for a trade and the mental ones for learning. They looked at him a little doubtfully. He was too handsome and too pleasant to be wasting his life. But his own desire was taken at first as too shocking to be considered.

Joseph had found a field even more thrilling to his romance-hungry soul than the bright pages of novels. It was all the drama of the books acted out for you, enchanting, intoxicating—the theater. If the Puritan way of thought found novels abhorrent, the stage was perdition itself. There were some forthright opinions expressed, the kind of remarks one feels free to say only to members of one's family, where they can be treasured up properly. But Joseph's mother, although firm in her disapproval, thought of a few little things she was Christian enough to forgive some Galway folks for, and gave her consent. He was her son; he would surely, somehow, turn out all right.

There is always a stage-struck kid or so hanging around every theater, but Joseph Henry was a most extraordinary person who had not found himself. His efforts to do so, in a field that he could happily focus all his attention on, were most successful. John Bernard, a British-born New York actor, had recently come up the river to Albany, where so much was going on with the war, and gotten a reluctant permission from the town council to open a theater. At first located in a hall called Thespian Hotel, near Clinton Avenue, his company was so popular that he was able to build the first theater in Albany, on the west side of Green Street, south of Hamilton. Opening on January 13, 1813, his troupe had presented such plays as *West Indian*, *Fortune's Frolic*, and *The Contrast*.

Joseph Henry was completely at home in the theater. He polished the glass shades protecting the candles that were their footlights (and made moonlight scenes so popular and successful) as happily as he acted a small part or ran to the tavern for ale or devised some clever stage effect. He was on the friendliest of terms with the actors and actresses, Samuel Drake, Ann Denney, and Henry Placide, and with William Dunlop, the playwright and painter, who had failed with a theatrical group in Albany ten years before and was so well acquainted in the world of the arts that he was called the American Vasari.

His enthusiasm even carried into an amateur society which called itself the Rostrum and was supposedly a debating society. For the edification of the group, however, he made a short story into a play and wrote an original one-acter, so it would seem more emotion than logic was displayed at the meetings.

This was a supremely happy time. And then one of those blessings in disguise came along and upset his whole life.

He had to stay indoors for a while with a minor face injury, and restless, looking for something to do, he picked up a book left on the parlor table by one of his mother's boarders. Up to now Joseph Henry must have seemed rather pathetic, a little strange even, but that was because his talents were so unusual for his time that no hint of a challenge had come to awaken them. He had been seduced by Beauty and now he was to be overwhelmed, drugged, and carried off forever by Truth.

Lectures On Experimental Philosophy, Astronomy and Chemistry, intended chiefly for the use of students and young persons, the title page said, by G. Gregory, D.D., Vicar of West-Ham, published in London in 1808. He thumbed through it and a paragraph caught his attention: *You throw a stone, or shoot an arrow upward into the air; why does it not go forward in the line or direction that you give it? Why does it stop at a certain distance, and then return to you? What force is it that pulls it down to the earth again, instead of its going onwards? On the contrary, Why does flame or smoke always mount upwards, though no force is used to send them in that direction? And why should not the flame of a candle drop toward the floor, when you reverse it or hold it downwards, instead of turning up and ascending into the air?*

He was almost stunned. To think about anything like this had never occurred to him. Why—all these things operated by laws that were forever the same, always true, no matter what. He read the book through again and again, each time more delighted by the prospect of everything making a glorious, irrefutable sense at last. He was almost eighteen years old and at last it had penetrated his skull that he had to have an education.[3]

Be Kind to the Likes of Joe Henry

He was to suffer all his life for his inability to make decisions, but here was a cause of action so plainly necessary that there was no decision to make. He quit the Green Street Theater; he made a passionate farewell speech to the Rostrum, resigning as president and expressing his new-found devotion to learning. To his mother it probably seemed too good to last, but inside of three years he had graduated from the Albany Academy, most of the time paying his way by teaching in a country school for fifteen dollars a month, and had been hired as tutor for the children of Patroon Van Rensselaer. In his free time he was reading La Grange's *Mécanique Analytique* and preparing papers for the Albany Institute of Science and Art that treated such subjects as "On the chemical and mechanical effects of steam: with experiments designed to illustrate the great reduction of temperature in steam of high elasticity when suddenly expanded."

NOTES TO CHAPTER THREE

1. Henry mentions that one day on the street in Albany a Negro came up to him and said he had been proud to work for Captain Billy Henry. Later this was interpreted to mean that his father had been a sea captain, although no other substantiation for such an occupation can be found. Those unfamiliar with the language of Negro laborers of even a generation ago are referred to the old Negro work songs: "John Henry say to the captain, 'A man ain't nothin' but a man,'" and "Take this hammer, take it to the captain; tell him I'm gone, boys; tell him I'm gone.'"

2. Henry was fond of telling stories of his childhood. This account of how he finally learned to read, and to like to read, appears in almost identical versions in a number of reminiscences written by his friends as a memorial following his death.

CHAPTER FOUR

Maury Afloat and Ashore

MAT'S FINE Virginia relatives were all that he had ever dreamed they'd be. For years he was to talk fondly of Tennessee and speak of himself as a plain, unpretentious frontiersman, but his heart was in Virginia and so was his loyalty. He *had* to amount to something, to prove that the Westerner belonged with these, to him, so-admirable people. He met his cousin and sister-in-law Eliza and her two little boys who lived with Dabney Herndon and his Maury wife in Fredericksburg. This Dabney had a brother Edward Herndon who was president of the Fredericksburg bank and about the richest man in the county. We note this Edward Herndon, Mat's uncle by marriage, because he had a daughter named Ann Hull, called Nannie. She was skinny, humorless, redhaired, wore glasses, and was as silent by nature as if she had been struck dumb, but she was a good and pious soul. And rich. There were other relatives that he met, of course, a redundancy as a matter of fact, both sides of his family running to eight or nine children as a rule.

Mat had to go on to Washington, to report at the Navy Department, then to Under Secretary of the Navy S. L. Southard, for orders. To his delight he was ordered to New York to report on board the recently completed frigate *Brandywine*. The *Brandywine* had been named for a Revolutionary War battle in which Lafayette had been wounded, and was presently to carry the old chevalier home to France after his most recent visit to the United States.

New York was a wonderful place in 1825, especially after the disappointment poor little Washington had been. Mat's black navy shoes trod the dirt of Broadway, arattle with carriages and coaches, lined with shopwindows dazzling with luxurious wares, the busy passers-by all looking so self-assured, even the little newsboys. And at Packet Row, on South Street were the ships that had sailed all over the world, nose to, with their carved figureheads projecting over the street. No clippers, these packets were heavily built and deep hulled, made to carry great cargoes and great loads of canvas. At the busy Navy Yard was the *Brandywine*, his ship, a frigate of forty-four guns and a crew of 480.

Life in the United States Navy at that time, while superior to service in the navies of other countries, was a dangerous and hard one. On Mat's first voyage the new *Brandywine* popped a quantity of her caulking and almost had to make an embarrassing return to Hampton Roads with her distinguished passenger. But Captain Charles Morris was an old sea dog and since her seams didn't literally open up they kept up with the trouble by a constant succession of jury-rigged repairs. Then they ran into a storm and Mat and the honored guest both became so seasick that they didn't care whether they made port or not. The "Roaring" *Brandywine* plowed on, as if she had at last gotten seawise herself. After formally delivering Lafayette back to his

42

country the *Brandywine* went into Cowes and got recaulked. Then to the Mediterranean and Commodore John Rodgers's squadron on patrol duty between Gibraltar and Egypt, with Port Mahón, Minorca, as their base.

> *Oh, I lost my hat at Cape de Gat*
> *And where d'ye think I found it?*
> *Behind a stone at Port Mahón*
> *With three pretty girls around it!*

This was the gravy run, keeping watch on the Barbary Corsairs and enjoying frequent shore leaves in sunny, English-influenced, Spanish-owned Port Mahón where the clean, bright-painted houses marched up hills as steep as in Fredericksburg, all the sun-glare angles softened with bougainvillaea and jasmine.[1] But Mat's life was not all that he might have wished; this was no atmosphere for the academic turn of mind. No teachers worthy of the name were ever provided. Mat found that he had to educate himself. It was easy to learn Spanish in the friendly base port, but subjects such as calculus and spherical geometry took some effort.

In "White Jacket," Herman Melville, who served as a sailor on board the *United States* and hated every moment of it, described the life of a "reefer" at that time:

Now come the "reefers," otherwise "middies" or midshipmen. These boys are sent to sea, for the purpose of making commodores; and in order to become commodores, many of them deem it indispensable forthwith to commence chewing tobacco, drinking brandy and water and swearing at the sailors. As they are only placed on board a seagoing ship to go to school and learn the duty of a lieutenant; and until qualified to act as such, have few or no special functions to attend to; they are little more, while midshipmen, than supernumeraries on board. Hence, in a crowded frigate, they are so everlasting crossing the path of both men and officers, that in the navy it has become a proverb, that a useless fellow is "as much in the way as a reefer."

In a gale of wind, when all hands are called and the deck swarms with men, the little 'middies' running about distracted and having nothing particular to do, make it up in vociferous swearing; exploding all about under foot like torpedoes. Some of them are terrible little boys, cocking their caps at alarming angles, and looking fierce as young roosters. They are generally great consumers of Macassar Oil and the Balm of Columbia; they thirst and rage after whiskers; and sometimes, applying their ointments, lay themselves out in the sun, to promote the fertility of their chins.

As the only way to learn to command, is to learn to obey, the usage of a ship of war is such that the midshipmen are constantly being ordered about by the lieutenants; though without having assigned them their particular destinations, they are always going somewhere and never arriving. In some things, they almost have a harder time of it than the seamen themselves. They are messengers and errand boys to their superiors.

"Mr. Pert," cries an officer of the deck, hailing a young gentleman forward. Mr. Pert advances, touches his hat, and remains in an attitude of deferential suspense. "Go forward and tell the boatswain I want him." And with this perilous errand, the middy hurries away, looking proud as a king.

The middies live by themselves in the steerage, where, nowadays, they dine off a table spread with a cloth. They have a castor at dinner; they have some other little boys (selected from the ship's company) to wait upon them; they sometimes drink coffee out of china. But for all these, their modern refinements, in some instances the affairs of their club go sadly to rack and ruin. The china is broken, the japanned coffee-pot dented like a pewter mug in an ale-house; the pronged forks resemble toothpicks (for which they are sometimes used) ; the table-knives are hacked into handsaws; and the cloth goes to the sailmaker to be patched.

44

Indeed, they are something like collegiate freshmen and sophomores, living in the college buildings, especially so far as the noise they make in their quarters is concerned. The steerage buzzes, hums, and swarms like a hive; or like an infant-school on a hot day, when the school mistress falls asleep with a fly on her nose.

In frigates, the ward-room—the retreat of the lieutenants —immediately adjoining the steerage, is on the same deck with it. Frequently, when the middies, waking early of a morning, as most youngsters do, would be kicking up their heels in their hammocks, or running about with double-reefed nightgowns, playing *tag* among the "clews"; the senior lieutenant would burst among them with a—"Young gentlemen, I am astonished. You must stop this sky-larking. Mr. Pert, what are you doing at the table there without your pantaloon? To your hammock, sir. Let me see no more of this. If you disturb the ward-room again, young gentlemen, you shall hear of it." And so saying, this hoary-headed senior lieutenant would retire to his cot in his state-room, like the father of a numerous family after getting up in his dressing-gown and slippers, to quiet a daybreak tumult in his populous nursery.

Back they went to New York in the spring of 1826, and then Mat was transferred to the frigate *Macedonian* (which had been a British ship prior to running afoul the above-mentioned *United States* during the War of 1812), and south they went to Rio, and then around the Horn. In March of 1827 he was transferred to the second-class sloop *Vincennes*, 18 guns. They were kept on duty up and down the coast of South America, protecting American property during the revolutions that were continually upsetting those long-downtrodden people, while Mat got to keep up his Spanish and learn the ways of small flirtations and the taste of candied rose petals (Tennessee was never like this!) under the Southern Cross.

45

Then the *Vincennes*, under Captain William Finch, started back to the States the *long way*. No ship of the United States Navy had yet circumnavigated the globe. Three weeks later they dropped anchor in Comptroller Bay at Nukahiva. Mat looked with shining eyes upon the tall mountain rib, the waterfalls, the palm trees, the transparent water over the coral reefs, and the smiling, handsome natives who had almost eaten his brother. Here was adventure and romance. With the chaplain he went ashore and talked to natives who said they remembered his brother. One old chief offered him a bride (as soon as they could capture one from the neighboring tribe) and wanted to make him his heir, Mat remembered years later.

To Hawaii, calling it the Sandwich Islands, they went, and thence across the Pacific to Macao, the Portuguese port that handled the Canton trade. And oh, the strange people! Not handsome like the Polynesians, but other-world, with bound feet and pigtails, the men in skirts and the women in trousers, eating boiled puppy dog and birds' nests, and making beautiful china and packing exotic teas with names like wind chimes. But they could not stay, being so long in the going, and headed for polyglot Manila, and thence to the Straits of Sunda, and Cape Town at the foot of Table Mountain. Their next stop was St. Helena, to take on water and see the tomb of Napoleon and Longwood, the house in which he died. And then across the Atlantic to New York, arriving June 8, 1830, to cheers and congratulations.

Mat now had to prepare for his exams for the rank of lieutenant. Actually, even after he passed he still would not be a lieutenant. His rank would be Passed Midshipman. But he would get nine hundred fifty dollars a year instead of the reefer's four hundred, and he would be eligible for promotion to lieutenant upon a vacancy occurring in the service.

Not being assigned to a ship, Mat went to Washington

to stay with some of his endless chain of relatives, and study for his exams. Quite by accident redhaired, blue-eyed, silent Nannie Herndon was also visiting in Washington. She was nineteen and had either improved in looks or Mat's brains had softened under the heavy load of studies and the influence of his rich relatives' suggestions. He wrote to Dick for advice, but got no answer. Somewhat to his later regret [2] he got himself, as he put it, shackled. He also passed his exams fourteenth from the bottom in a group of forty. He could have expected this latter mishap. He hated to learn by rote so he refused to memorize "the words in the book." The fact that he understood Bowditch's *New American Practical Navigator* and could work the problems called for only partly made up for his not being able to rattle off the rules. He had gone to the exam knowing that the hated "words in the book" were wanted, but he couldn't make himself conform.

They were talking nullification in the South now, the asserted right of a state to refuse to allow a federal law to be enforced within its borders. Some were even talking secession, as the Yankees had a few years back, and for the same reason: states' rights. Economic differences between North and South were growing more pronounced, the two regions were drifting apart. There were many who felt that one set of laws wouldn't fit both of them.

In June of 1831, engaged to Nannie Herndon with the blessings of all, Passed Midshipman Maury was assigned to the war sloop *Falmouth*, 18 guns, as sailing master, and set sail for Valparaiso, Chile. His skylarking reefer days over, he was responsible for the navigation of the ship. In his innocence, since he wanted to break all speed records and establish that reputation he longed for, he looked for charts of currents and winds as well as tides and coast lines. There were none.

"Why not?"

"Don't ask me. Naval officers don't bother with such rubbish."

"Why not?"

"It just isn't *done*."

The patrol of the Pacific coast of South America went on, relieved now and then with stays in crumbling old Spanish ports that were still alive enough to offer music, dancing, *aguardiente*, moonlight shining through palm leaves, and beautiful señoritas with roses in their hair. During lulls in the local wars, that was. Of course, Mat was true to that plain little redhead back home. His belief in himself as a gentleman, absurd as it was to make him look at times, guaranteed his behavior even when no one was watching.

From the *Falmouth* he was transferred to the schooner *Dolphin* for a few weeks, then in the fall of 1833 to the frigate *Potomac*, under his brother's former commander on the *Essex Junior*, Captain John Downes. And now it was home again, after four more years at sea, and very little money and few prospects for more.

Leaving the *Potomac* at Boston, Mat went to Fredericksburg and was married to Ann Hull Herndon on July 15, 1834.

Mat had been brought up in the belief that a fair amount of brains, coupled with industry and perseverance, will bring you to success. It will, if you don't want much. If you want more, you have to add the ability to promote, to pull wires and lay traps, and be two steps ahead of the game. For the heights of success, however, you must have big friends, important friends, friends in the right places.

In the Navy of Mat's time all this was as true as it had been in the navy of Themistocles. If Mat had a motto, it was Persevere and Prosper. He was bright, and not afraid of work. He could scheme with the best of them. But in his father's house the book that stood next to the Bible was Bunyan's *Pilgrim's Progress*. If ever Mr.-Valiant-For-Truth walked this earth it was Mat Maury. If something was wrong, he *would* speak out against it. The number of dolts and dotards with important connections whose feelings were injured by Mat's outspokenness was legion. Those who said he would amount to something someday evoked incredulous laughter.

His entire naval career was shot through with disappointments. "Logan" Porter, who might have been expected to befriend him, had had to resign. John Downes was never important and David Farragut was a mere lieutenant still, and those who were impressed by him were never in the right places.

And all too often, it must be admitted, he was found to be an advocate of doing things the right way instead of the Navy way.

He was a rebel, an innovator, a hater of sacred cows and *status quos*. After nine years of banging his head against the sturdy oak of naval tradition, he was placed on the inactive list on half pay and forgotten.

Well, nobody treated Matthew Fontaine Maury that way —and since they didn't seem to realize that important fact, he determined to show them.

He and Nannie moved into an unpretentious white frame house on Charlotte Street in Fredericksburg. His sister-in-law Eliza moved in with them, with her two boys: William Lewis, named for his father's old captain, who had disappeared along with the *Epervier* and all hands during the War of 1812, and Dabney Herndon, named for her husband's best friend, Nannie's uncle. By the time they were settled Nannie was pregnant, and since she and Mat were to have eight children, this would be her condition more often than not for quite a while.

For a long time Mat had considered the possibility of

49

writing a book on some scientific subject. None had ever been written by an officer of the United States Navy. He wrote an article on navigating Cape Horn that was printed in Silliman's *Journal*, the best-known American journal of science; it had carried an article by one Joseph Henry a little while before. Maury's didn't cause the furor that Henry's did, but it encouraged him to go on with his writing.

Concurrently he had a grievance with the Secretary of the Navy, Mahlon Dickerson, and reported him to the President, that good Tennessean Andrew Jackson, which did him little good in terms of his career. It also made him afraid to trust the Navy with the completed manuscript of his scientific book.[3] He had written the first work on the science of navigation (or, for that matter, the science of anything) by an American naval officer, so he thought it would get him someplace; it had been written with that solely in mind. He assumed that he would be made a lieutenant of ten years' standing at least, with five thousand dollars in back pay as reward. However, he also had insulted the Secretary of the Navy. President Jackson saw to it that Mat was promoted to lieutenant on June 10, 1836; but Secretary Dickerson saw to it that Mat got no back pay, that he had to pay for the entire publication of the book himself, and that he was left on the inactive list on half pay.

These conflicts shook up Mat's personal life as well as his Navy life. He would be able to talk on no other subject than his grievance, nor to pay attention to others unless they were discussing it. It absorbed him completely. To his advantage, a great deal of good could be done at this time by someone criticizing the Navy, which had wilted into peacetime dry rot. It needed a complete overhauling. And Mat was angry and tactless enough to start going over in his mind things he would like to say.

Mahlon Dickerson was a cut above the average Secretary

of the Navy, ostensibly a loyal Jacksonian to the core. He had his own pride and a wide field of resentment to operate in. In mid-1836 President Jackson had been talked into having the government sponsor an exploring expedition to the Pacific, to call the world's attention to our scientific endeavors. Dickerson knew this expensive project had been foisted onto the Navy by Yankee whaling interests who wanted the war-loving natives of the South Pacific islands to be impressed by powerful United States fighting ships. And, maybe, to be pushed around just a little bit, so they'd respect American commercial vessels more. Dickerson had to appear to go along with it, however.

The *Macedonian* was ordered to take part, also two brigs, all under Captain Thomas ap Catesby Jones.

Then everything went wrong: an assortment of delays and mishaps and foulups, some of which were Dickerson's fault, and some not.

Captain Jones requested that Mat be assigned to his command, but he neglected to ask him personally first. Mat thought this discourteous and refused the assignment, ruffling his feathers mightily. Then Captain Dormin, who had been a fellow officer on some of Mat's early cruises, asked if he would be his first on the new store ship, *Relief*, now being completed for the expedition. Mat (who signed his letters to Dormin in Spanish, *"Hasta Luego, Matéo"*) accepted, believing that all was settled.

The delays continued. Contradictory and vexatious orders poured upon Captain Jones in such quantity that his health broke down and he was forced to resign. Mat was ordered from the *Relief* to the *Macedonian* and as junior officer at that, which he furiously declined, asking to be put on furlough and demanding more apologies from the Secretary. Then he was appointed astronomer to the expedition. Thinking of the importance of astronomy in navigation Mat went amicably to Philadelphia where the astronomical and other instruments were being assembled at the Navy Yard. From Professor Johnson he learned the second-splitting mysteries of sidereal time and the incessant procession of the equinoxes, and about the planets, which are not stars, and the suns, which are.[4] He also got pretty well convinced that the expedition could not possibly get all its scientific equipment together by the fall of 1837, the latest departure date. Some of it hadn't even been made yet, particularly for the hydrographical section.

And so it turned out. More delays. By this time he had refused the post of astronomer, because it would hazard his reputation to enter a field so barren.[5] He wanted to be hydrographer now, or joint hydrographer-astronomer. The Navy wanted him to do the regular duties of a lieutenant and be astronomer for the expedition on the side.

Now the name of Charles Wilkes, head of the Depot of Charts and Instruments, an astronomer, began to be rumored for that of commander of the expedition. Mat had met Wilkes only to exchange unpleasantries, and Mat told him now that if he were put in charge of the exploring expedition he would not go. He would never cooperate with Wilkes in any way, he said bluntly. By now it had gotten to be 1838.

Wilkes, a junior lieutenant, was married to a sister of the architect James Renwick. This Renwick was Washington Irving's best friend and Washington Irving was James K. Paulding's brother-in-law, and James K. Paulding was the new Secretary of the Navy, appointed by his friend, the new President, Martin Van Buren. New York was running the show now, not Tennessee.

The United States Exploring Expedition got under way August 10, 1838, with the old *Vincennes*, another sloop of war, the *Peacock*, a brig, the *Porpoise*, the store ship *Relief*

and two tenders, the *Gull* and the *Flying Fish*. In passing
we note that the expedition brought back enough flora,
fauna, and mineralogical specimens to found a museum, that
they killed an impressive number of natives and bodily carried off a chief, and give as one example of the cooperation
between the Navy and the scientists (civilian) they took
along: the botanists were told they could have the day to go
ashore and botanize, but they had to bring back enough
celery to feed the entire crew! Commanding the expedition
was Lieutenant Charles Wilkes, seventieth from the bottom
of the Navy List.

Naturally Mat exploded loudly and at length. He and
Nannie were put to it to make ends meet on his half pay.
He had been doing some lecturing on scientific subjects, and
acting as superintendent of a mine near Fredericksburg.
Now he thought of writing again. He angrily composed a
series of articles for one of the Richmond papers, the *Whig*,
about the injustices of the government in handling the Exploring Expedition. That the Honorable James K. Paulding, whom he called upon to right these wrongs, was actually
their author seems to have been unknown to him. At the
time of the Wilkes appointment Mahlon Dickerson had still
been Secretary of the Navy, but Paulding had almost immediately replaced him, and had done nothing to remove
Wilkes. He had had ample opportunity to do so and ample
urging from a number of naval officers in addition to Maury
who protested the appointment. There seems little doubt
that Dickerson had been getting orders from the President
again. They had even rung in Joel R. Poinsett, the Secretary of War, as one of Wilkes's sponsors. It was an Administration deal, pure and simple, and in violation of law, as
Maury pointed out in his newspaper articles.

Mat signed these articles "Harry Bluff, U.S.N.," and
went on to belabor the Navy and the powers that be with

more unpalatable truth in the *Whig* signed "Will Watch"
and "Brandywine." No one was disposed to do anything
about the wrongs he brought out, or not right away, any-
how. The disgruntled naval officers couldn't even get a round
robin of protest together about the Wilkes appointment,
though Mat tried hard to get someone else to start one. But
the Harry Bluff articles had staying power. The wasteful
expenditure of money on naval repairs as then handled, the
lack of a Navy school to match the Army one at West Point,
and the need for changes in various regulations were all
legitimate targets for criticism.

Although Mat disavowed all knowledge of the identity of
the *Whig* articles' author, it must have been fairly obvious
to everyone that he was the one. At any rate, just as he was
really getting going, he was put back on active duty, to help
survey the harbors along the Carolina and Georgia coasts.
Ordered to Portsmouth, he was allowed to wait until everything else was ready, then assigned to the steamboat *Engineer*. They had a regular little expedition of their own, with
Lieutenant James Glynn in charge from on board the
schooner *Experiment*. That it was a loathsome task, Mat
made no bones. He had to take soundings while Glynn did
the tidal measurements. In other words, he had to work instead of give orders, the way a Navy officer should. But as
the unhealthy season soon came on, they were ordered back
to Hampton Roads and Mat was allowed a month's leave.
When he discovered that he was to report back to Lieutenant
Glynn after his leave, this time at New York to board the
brig *Consort* for more surveying, he cried that this was
odious work and wondered why *he*, of all people, had been
chosen for it.

After a visit with his parents back in Tennessee, during
which he helped them get ready to spend the winter with

54

his sister Matilda, now Mrs. Holland, in Mississippi, he started the northern way for New York. It was latish in October 1839. He was thirty-three years old and in the prime of health and mental alertness. The stagecoach he was riding went off the road at night in a rainstorm and turned over. Of the thirteen people aboard, he was the only one injured. His right thighbone was broken and his right knee dislocated. He was put to bed in a miserable tavern operated by one Jake Breakhell in Somerset, Ohio, and attended by two excellent physicians. The pair got it from him in the saltiest of naval language, but anyone who has had a dislocation reduced by pulling on a leg already broken, and without anesthesia, could only cheer him on. Another of his wards, harum-scarum John Minor, came from Fredericksburg to take care of him for a few days and Nannie started but got sick on the way and thankfully returned home. A little boy of thirteen was hired to cook and fetch and carry for him, and soon John Minor went back and left Mat alone, with a French grammar to study. His only compensation was in not having to go to sea with Glynn on the *Consort*. This miserable place, the bare room with its three pieces of rickety furniture, the fireplace with no fender to keep sparks from flying onto the floor, one stinking tallow candle by night, a cigar box for a desk, the terrible food, all helped to depress him. He had plenty of loud arguments with the landlord and his shiftless servant and plenty of time for sobering contemplation.

He had, up to now, played very fair with his writing about the Navy. Every word had been just as true as he knew how to write; not one effort had been made to put himself forward; where he had seen wrong he had been bold enough to speak out against it. It had gotten him to this miserable, dirty, white-trash Phoenix Tavern.

The two doctors talked encouragingly. They thought he would be able to walk again. He might limp, though; might have to use a cane.

I will never go to sea again. He looked at the yellow smoke-stained muslin tacked to the rafters overhead to make a ceiling. He had seen the sky look like that when the air was heavy with dust blown up from far-off Africa. That was something that wasn't in the books; no one had ever explained the sea and its wonders, overpainting them in the colors of superstition and so hidden, so ignored. And those who sneered at superstition also sneered at the common seaman's work involved in trying to discover accurate answers. Forgetting his own complaints about having to do such work, he could dream as he pleased. Oh, to seize upon those answers, answers all beautiful and shining because they were God's truth, and shove them down all those sneering Navy throats. But these were dreams and he was helpless, possibly crippled forever. And with a wife and two little daughters to support, John Minor to keep in hand, Lewis and Dabney needing his advice and encouragement, and their mother wanting to be with them. He loved his family, he knew, far more than anything else.

And all he possessed in this world was the rank of lieutenant in the United States Navy—and such as he had in the way of brains for learning and putting what he had observed to work for him. He began to plan far, far ahead. Because he had to. Because he was frightened.

It was three months before he could be moved, with his leg encased in a hardened mass of binder's board soaked in glue, to the home of his half-English cousins, the Maury tobacco merchants, on Fourth Street, in New York. They were the children of his father's elder brother James, who had been in the consular service and had married Margaret Rutson of Liverpool. Ann wrote books and raised her brother

Mat's children after his beautiful and talented wife (Sarah Mytton Maury, also the author of several books) died, and kept house for her elderly father and bachelor brother Rutson, and was a very fat, thoroughly contented spinster lady. Rutson Maury was to be the most loyal and quite possibly the least appreciated friend that a nationally-denounced figure ever had.

They finally got Mat home to Fredericksburg, Nannie got pregnant again, the Navy offered to lend Mat to the Coast Survey (he was still on crutches) as an instrument man, and things were normal. Imprisoned in the house, he went over and over his problem of what to do. He had to make a place for himself to fill, and creditably. He was conscious of an ignorance so vast that it sickened him, he said in a letter to his cousin Ann at this time. But he was not ignorant of what was wrong with the Navy. He was very popular; he had many friends—so far none of them had been able to help him, but they took the Navy apart and put it back together again, improved, in their talks and letters. Mat knew he had only dented the surface with his "Will Watch" and "Harry Bluff" articles in the *Whig*. Those articles had brought attention to him. And now the naval brass could not shut him up by sending him on any dirty job at sea, because he was crippled. Last year, before his accident, he had written an article on improving the commerce of the South, which had been published in the *Southern Literary Messenger*, then an important magazine. That it had been read, he knew, because in it he had advocated great-circle sailing, and shortly thereafter the British had come out with a highly praised work on the subject. One might think from reading Maury that he discovered great-circle sailing; actually, globes had been carried on ships for hundreds of years and the first mention of great-circle routes occurs in preserved records in 1594.[6]

The first in a series of naval reform articles under the heading, "Scraps from the Lucky Bag," appeared in the April 1840 *Southern Literary Messenger*. They appeared from time to time, all signed "Harry Bluff," for two years. Widely reprinted and widely read, they covered as many subjects as might be found in a ship's "Lucky Bag," he explained, that being where all the articles left on the berth deck of a ship are placed after being confiscated, and made available to anyone who wants them. Among his projected reforms he proposed abolition of the Navy Board of Commissioners and to institute bureaus, each with a separate responsibility, and creation of the post of Assistant Secretary of the Navy for a top-ranking naval officer. This would do away with the politics and graft so common in naval circles, he pointed out. He published figures to prove that the waste in building and repairing ships was prodigious and that this extra money was going into someone's pocket, instead of buying things for the Navy. He went over other reforms he had suggested in the Richmond *Whig* articles: starting a naval academy; reorganizing the system of ranks among naval officers to give the United States Navy titles equal to those held by officers of other seafaring nations; he wanted to have Pensacola fortified, more steamships commissioned.

Secretary of the Navy Paulding, who had helped on Washington Irving's *Salmagundi* papers and had himself composed "Peter Piper picked a peck of pickled peppers," might have had his own opinion of Maury both as a writer and as a naval officer. Steam indeed! When his political supporters were in the business of building the world's finest sailing ships? That was only one instance where nothing was done in the way of carrying out Maury's recommendations. Still, these gibes of Mat's, these captious, nagging "Scraps" that kept appearing and then reappearing, some of them even being reprinted in the *Army and Navy Chron-*

icle, had a surprising staying power. People began to get
the idea that there was something wrong with the Navy.

The *Southern Literary Messenger* for July 1841 published an article about Maury, signed "A Brother Officer,"
which read as if written by a blood relative who owed Mat
money. Among the many adulatory paragraphs was one
praising him for inventing a new device to measure lunar
distances, which Mat had written up in Silliman's *Journal*
several years before, and which the Navy had neglected to
adopt. It went on to praise Maury for trying to get southern
commerce to navigate with steam to offset the sea trade by
Yankees with their packet lines, but the South refused to go
in for any kind of shipping. It concluded: "His patriotic
heart will do much . . . to erect the beacon of hope amidst
the darkest pavilion of the waters."

Life in the Maury house was the usual series of family
crises. His children—Elizabeth Herndon, called Betty;
Diana Fontaine, called Little Nannie by the family and
Curly by her pa; and Richard Lancelot, called Dick by the
family and Goggin by his father—alternately spoiled and
spanked, were growing up rather more under the influence
of the spoiling. His nephew Lewis had shown great promise
but an unfortunate heart condition had exposed him to the
doctors at a time when they were pouring boiling water on
the chest of coronary sufferers to stimulate the action of the
heart,[7] and it carried him off. Dabney was now studying law
at the University of Virginia and while he disliked the subject he kept at it to please his uncle.[8] The obstreperous John
Minor was about to be sent off to sea as a midshipman under
the iron hand of Captain "Mad Jack" Percival, and two
more cousin's children had been taken in, Sallie Fontaine
Maury and Ellen Maury. Silent Big Nannie and Sister
Eliza did the sewing and the housetending and taught the
children their early lessons. Mat wrote more articles for and

acted as assistant editor of the *Southern Literary Messenger*, and although he had finished the naval reform series he still expected it to do him good. A Virginian, John Tyler, was now in the White House and had recently dismissed almost his entire Cabinet. Among his new appointments had been another Virginian, Abel Upshur, as Secretary of the Navy. If things were ever going to break for Mat Maury, now would seem to be the time.

According to several Maury biographers, Mat requested sea duty in the summer of 1841, but was thwarted by the action of friends who had several doctors write to Upshur's predecessor and state that Maury was not well enough for such an assignment. Later on Mat himself asserted that he never refused sea duty. If so, it becomes difficult to explain this letter:

18 November, 1841. To Hon. A. P. Upshur, Secretary of the Navy, Washington City. In reply to your letter of the 13th instant and its Enclosure herewith returned, I beg leave to say that the opinion expressed by my friends Doctors Browne, Carmichael and Wellford, induces me to violate a rule of my own, by asking to be relieved from order to sea. I am respectfully, your obdt. sevt. M. F. Maury. Lt. U. S. Navy.

Apparently Secretary of the Navy Upshur, who was one of the men responsible for getting the Navy out of sails and into steam, accepted Maury as one of the Right Crowd, because nothing was made of Maury's renig. Upshur even had *Maury on Navigation* listed in the naval station bills of the time as the second thing the captain grabbed (first was the compass) on having to take to the boats. So it would seem that at least for a while the great work of the Yankee Nathaniel Bowditch had been superseded by the Virginian's text. Besides putting Maury's second-rate book on navigation on all ships of the United States Navy in place of Bowditch's great classic, Upshur had more and better to offer Maury, but it took a while to organize. It was necessary to get Congress to pass an act abolishing the Naval Board and setting up a system of bureaus. This reform Upshur began to push, and also a request for an appropriation to enlarge the Depot of Charts and Instruments and to build an observatory.

Mat now was very, very careful to keep in good standing with everybody. He wrote his cousin Rutson in February of 1842 that he had heard some vague rumors that he might be put in charge of the Hydrographic Office if the reorganization was effected. He also protested sharply against pulling wires to get himself advancement and then added, apparently overcome by a fit of frankness, that he might pull a few.

On July 1, 1842, he was put in charge of the Depot of Charts and Instruments. Leaving Nannie at home, pregnant, he went to Washington to take up his new duties. From his grand ambition of being made a captain and heading one of the planned bureaus he had to accept the orphan and neglected Chart Depot. Well, that was always the way it was: second best. And yet in those dusty, mildewed logbooks which were jammed and piled in closets and basements and lumber rooms and always seemed to be spilling out to annoy him, there lay the uncompiled answers to questions he had long pondered over, answers that were to make Mat Maury famous.

NOTES TO CHAPTER FOUR

1. Robert Grave's article on Minorca in the January 1960 *Holiday* describes the activities of the British fleet at length in

Port Mahón, never mentioning a word about the American use of this port.

2. Letter to his brother Richard, November 17, 1831. In this he also mentions that he gets only $700 a year but will advance to $950. He complains bitterly about the slowness of promotion.

3. Letter to James Maury, November 19, 1834, and one to his brother Richard, October 29, 1835. The book was *A New Theoretical Practical Treatise on Navigation, etc.*, by M. F. Maury, Passed Midshipman, United States Navy.

4. All of his letters of this period are on the subject of the exploring expedition. To his cousin Ann Maury on December 23, 1836, about his insult by Captain Jones. To her again on July 5, 1837, about the insult of being ordered to the *Macedonian:* "I will not go after having been trifled with as I have been by the Dept. unless atonement is made by that weak old man at its head." From Philadelphia September 19, 1837, to Captain Dormin, saying he is studying astronomy at an observatory on Rittenhouse Square.

5. To Captain Dormin, November 11, 1837.

6. *The Sailing Ships of New England*, Robinson and Dow.

7. Or you could have a woolly mass of dry wormwood leaves spread on your chest and then set fire to. This was standard practice of the time. Dabney describes his brother's treatment and how it distressed his uncle (no doubt it distressed poor Lewis, too!) in his *Recollections of a Virginian.*

8. After graduating from the University Dabney was appointed to West Point and so saved from being a lawyer, for which he admits he had no talent. See his *Recollections of a Virginian.*

(Note: There is plenty in Maury's correspondence at this time to indicate an attraction for, if not an infatuation with, his fat but pretty cousin Ann. However, Maury was too completely the egotist ever to give up anything for a woman. There are even small slaps at Big Nannie, saying that once she blessed him and now cheers and comforts him in a letter to Sarah Mytton Maury, November 14, 1846.)

CHAPTER FIVE

Henry Invents Some Things Familiar to Us

AFTER JOSEPH HENRY finished his education he spent nine years trying to find the niche in which he belonged. He tutored the Van Rensselaer children, who were to be involved in the anti-rent wars when they found the patroon's tenants owed $400,000 in back rent after his death and didn't intend to pay it. He tutored young Henry James, who later fathered those two giants, William and the second Henry, after the boy had had a foot amputated following a severe burn.[1] He acted as librarian for the town science and art society and gave lectures and demonstrations on scientific subjects for it. He helped Dr. T. Romeyn Beck, head of the Albany Academy, set up his experiments to demonstrate to his natural-philosophy classes the known principles of physics. He studied medicine under Dr. Tully and Dr. Marsh. Then, not having discovered any goal worth struggling for, he began to suffer what appeared to be a nervous breakdown; he lost weight; he was unable to sleep; his mind was filled with wild fancies.

Stephen Van Rensselaer seems to have been Joseph Henry's good angel; now that things were all muddled up again and life seemed as useless as it had at Galway, and his mother saw him wasting away with the white plague as his father had, the patroon stepped in. He got a local judge named Conkling to have Joseph appointed surveyor on a projected state road to run from Kingston on the Hudson to Portland Harbor on Lake Erie. The winter of 1825–26, which was so delightful in Port Mahón, Minorca, proved a Catskill winter was no slouch, even compared to the Adirondack ones, and Joseph got shaken back into shape as he walked and climbed over some three hundred miles of rough country pursuing his rodman and chainman with a surveying instrument. He met Amos Eaton, the American geologist who had read the early essays of Charles Lyell and expounded his new theories of a slow, millions-of-years-long history of the earth's surface features. Always before, with the Bible in mind, scientists had propounded the theory of a series of cataclysmic changes. Eaton was fascinated by the worn rocks, the fossils, the signs of glaciation, the physical proof of this theory. Joseph Henry stored it up to think about, and kicked the fossils out of his way.

Back home that spring he found that the Albany Academy wanted him to accept a job as assistant teacher of mathematics. As one might have guessed, the patroon had been presiding officer of the Academy's Board of Trustees, but apparently it was the urging of the head of the school, Dr. T. Romeyn Beck, his old teacher, which pursuaded Joseph to accept.

The Board of Trustees of the Academy, which had been founded in 1813, had commissioned Philip Hooker to design

a building for them that would look as well as the fifteen
other public buildings he had created for the town in the
elegant but imposing post-colonial style. In a park in the
center of town where it would show to the best advantage,
the three-story brownstone building was one of the sights of
the town,[2] with simple Ionic pilasters, a balustraded parapet,
a second-floor entrance with double steps leading up to a
handsome fanlighted door, all topped with a graceful classic
cupola.

The Academy was said to be a college in disguise, but "it
began its work low down." [3] The new teacher taught seven
hours a day, half of that time instructing the rudiments of
arithmetic to a large class of small boys. Luckily for Joseph,
he was bigger than average, handsome in a completely mas-
culine way, and had learned during those years in the
theater how to give the impression that no nonsense would
be tolerated without, at the same time, making himself hated.
He thoroughly enjoyed teaching and its better half, that
insidious, fascinating atmosphere of the academic society,
which is habit forming. In 1827, under the direction of Dr.
Beck, Joseph began his first meteorological work. Each
academy in the state was furnished with a thermometer,
rain-gauge, and other instruments by the state board of
regents and required to send in reports on their readings.
Joseph made monthly and yearly abstracts of the findings
of these forty stations as to temperature, wind, rain, etc.,
and they were published in the annual reports the board of
regents made to the state legislature. The weather and
what made it fascinated him as they do so many in a land
where seven kinds of weather, most of it violent, can happen
in an hour, as if to show off the shining days in almost too
blinding a comparison. In 1828 he was appointed professor
of mathematics and natural philosophy at the academy.
From the very first, in his spare time, the short summer

vacation and the long hours after school, he had carried on a series of experiments with insignificant-looking iron bars and odd lengths of wire and snippets of what looked suspiciously like silk petticoat.

It was the year of the "tariff of abominations," which had been written by southern legislators so as to be too strict to be passed but would stain the pro-tariff reputations of those northerners who opposed it. The trick boomeranged: while nobody liked it, the bill was passed, so solid was the pro-tariff faction. The South then felt that the North would stop at nothing to injure it, and another wedge was driven into the fissure splitting the country.

Jackson had been elected president; his man Martin Van Buren was a power in Albany, and his party's newspaper, the Albany *Argus,* supported the measures that Van Buren's so-called Albany Regency wanted in Washington. Albany, despite depressions elsewhere, was booming with the continued prosperity of the recently-completed Erie Canal, which gave the back door of New York City a waterway through the Mohawk Valley to the Great Lakes and the center of the country. At the foot of State Street was the canal-boat basin where a 4,000-foot-long wharf with the weighmaster's building and many tall warehouses on it separated the river from the gray-stone lock area. Beyond rose the tall masts of the sailing ships that used Albany as a deep-water harbor. Here and there were to be seen the sturdy, ugly walking beams of the side-wheelers that carried the river trade.

Here on a pleasant Sunday afternoon one might have seen the dignified Professor Henry walking with a young lady, his first cousin and promised bride, Harriet Alexander. She was the daughter of his mother's well-to-do brother Alexander Alexander, mentioned earlier, who had lived in Schenectady until his death in 1809. Harriet and her mother and her brother Stephen, a recent graduate of Union College, had just moved to Albany. Stephen was teaching mathematics and astronomy at the Albany Academy and they had a pleasant circle of friends and relatives in the capital.

Harriet was small, oval-faced, even-featured, with large, intelligent-looking dark eyes and thick, dark-brown hair.[4] She was quick-witted, good-natured, frank, a devoted wife and mother, fond of friends and society, charitable to a fault. Abandoned babies were always being left at the door. She raised an orphan boy about whom nothing was known, founded a home for waifs, religiously visited the sick. She was also a tiny bit jealous of her husband, which he sometimes teased her about. As for her money, Joseph Henry never touched it, and wouldn't allow anyone else to, either.[5]

They were married in May of 1830. Harriet was eighteen and Joseph was thirty-two.

Meanwhile, at the Academy, Joseph Henry was by way of making a name for himself. Six years before he started tinkering around with the soft iron bar and the wire and silk the British scientist William Sturgeon had invented the electromagnet. It was a horseshoe-shaped piece of soft iron coated with shellac and wrapped with a few turns of bare wire. When hooked up to his crude little battery, this device would lift seven pounds. It was good for nothing but to play with and conjecture over. Ever since it had been invented people had been doing just that, some of them the most famous names in the history of science, but no one had been able to improve on it. Joseph Henry, his position comparable to that of the high-school teacher of today and his education considerably scantier, made the electromagnet into a workable reality. He wrapped the thin silk around the wire for insulation, then wrapped the wire closely and in layers around the horseshoe of soft iron. One of them, hooked up to a series of batteries, lifted four hundred times its own weight. The one he made especially for Yale University to use in its experimental laboratory would lift a ton. He wrote it up for Silliman's *Journal* in April 1831. It was the scientific wonder of its day. We take this spool- or bobbin-wound electromagnet completely for granted today, and yet it is one of the most-used components in our electronic civilization. There is one hidden under the screw-off cap of your telephone receiver.

Joseph Henry was one of those thriving shoots from the rare but hardy plant that had produced the great Franklin and the ingrate Count Rumford, someone to be encouraged to further demonstrations of genius. Union College gave him an honorary doctorate of laws. The Albany Academy allowed him to use a room in the basement for his experiments. The electromagnet began to be used in industry. Port Henry, where some of the richest iron ores in the world are mined, was named for Joseph Henry. For more than a hundred years after his discovery the magnetic ore was still being removed from crushed rock here by an electromagnet's passing over it. And so to the thousands of uses of today.

Joseph Henry did not patent this version of the electromagnet, although patents worth millions are granted for changes far more minor than the improvement he made on Sturgeon's little gadget. Henry had his own kind of pride. He had done the work on his own time and at his own expense, but the Academy had offered him the opportunity to make these experiments. He was not just Joseph Henry; he was connected in men's minds with the Albany Academy. He did his work under its roof and with its encouragement, such as it was. He could have resigned and set up his own laboratory and gone on with his work, but there was the chance that he might fail; he had been hungry and neglected once and that had been enough. So he gave up all thoughts of gain. Others were to become rich because he tended to abandon every project as soon as he had established the principle.

It was 1827 when he discovered his version of the electromagnet and 1831 before he published his findings. During these years he was continually working on new ideas. His sunny third-floor classroom was the scene of many demonstrations of electronic "firsts," spread out on the long, bare table at the head of the room, his audience only boys wriggling on the hard, backless schoolroom benches.

In 1830 he strung a length of wire around the room, hooked it up to his so-called "trough" battery and an electromagnet, and put the battery and the electromagnet on the big demonstration table. Between the open ends of the horseshoe-shaped electromagnet he put one end of a long, narrow bar magnet. This bar magnet pivoted from side to side freely. Near it he placed the kind of desk-top bell that one bangs on to make it sound. When the circuit was completed, the bar magnet, hooked up to *nothing*, swung around and sounded the bell loudly. As it stood, he had invented the electric doorbell because there was a limit to the performance depending on the length of the wire: beyond a certain distance the power fell off and the bar magnet didn't move. So Joseph made the first electrical relay. To him it was so elementary that he never even published his findings in a separate paper on the subject. He wound part of the long wire around a horseshoe magnet. Across the poles was an armature that moved when the circuit was closed. This movement opened a second circuit with another battery. Now, instead of fading away, the impulse went on its way unimpeded. There was no limit to the number of such relays that could be used. He could have sent that bell-ringing signal around the world: it was the first telegraph.

In Silliman's *Journal* for July 1831 a letter from Joseph

to Professor Silliman (Benjamin Silliman, editor and founder of the *American Journal of Science and Arts*, was the first professor of chemistry and natural philosophy at Yale) was printed. In it was an impressive sentence: *I have lately succeeded in producing motion in a little machine, by a power which I believe has never before been applied in mechanics, by magnet attraction and repulsion.* It was a toy to him, with possibilities that he never followed through, just as Sturgeon had done with the electromagnet. From it a Salisbury, Vermont, blacksmith named Thomas Davenport invented the first practical electric motor.

To take stock of what Joseph Henry contributed to the betterment of mankind, *so far* he had discovered the practical electromagnet, the electrical relay, the telegraph, and the electric motor. Not one of these did he take beyond the experimental stage; they were embryonic gifts for promoters to suffer with if they dared and grow rich with if they were lucky. Joseph was thirty-four. He had an ambition to be more than a poor, struggling high-school teacher, but not much more. A little fame, perhaps, that was more than the average fellow had, but the cheerful society of inquiring minds was worth more to him than all the things money had brought to the rich people he knew. Also, there was another discovery that he had been working on for years in conjunction with his other experiments, something so important that it would make his country famous because of him. It had to be right. Not partly right. Not disputable in any way. It had to be perfect. And possibly, when this great finding was published, he would be offered the job of his dreams, teaching in college.

This all-important project of his was to prove that magnetism produced electricity.

Everyone knew that electricity produced magnetism. Joseph's electromagnets demonstrated that every time they

were turned on. Now to rearrange those wires and batteries
and magnets some way so that a current would be induced
in the wire by the magnet. He wound a wire on itself around
the armature that connected the two legs of one of his
electromagnets and stuck each end of this spiral of wire
into cups of mercury. From the cups of mercury wires ran
to a galvanometer. Henry watched the needle of the galvanometer move back and forth as his assistant turned the
electromagnets' battery on and off.[6] He described his conclusion: *It appears that a current of electricity is produced
for an instant in a helix of copper wire surrounding a piece
of soft iron whenever magnetism is induced in the iron; and
a current in the opposite direction when the magnetic action
ceases; also that an instantaneous current in one or the other
direction accompanies every change in the magnetic intensity of the iron.*[7]

One can date this experiment from the equipment used in
it. Joseph Henry would seem to have been the first to see
proof that magnetism produces electricity. He discussed the
phenomenon with his friends and coworkers. He went over
and over it. He proved and reproved it to himself. But he
did not publish his findings.

This was not merely a new gadget or a useful machine he
had invented. He had discovered a new principle of physical
law. It was a triumph of reasoning, not a feat of mechanics.
But his overriding modesty made him hesitant about telling
anyone: supposing some famous scientist in some land across
the sea should laugh at him, and—by implication—at all of
us naïve Americans?

The April 1832 *Annals of Philosophy* carried a notice to
the effect that the British scientist Michael Faraday had
discovered the principle of magnetoelectricity.

Heartbreak came in all sorts of ways that year to the
little white frame house on Columbia Street where Joseph

and Harriet lived. The fame of first discovery had been denied to him. Worse, when he acceded to Benjamin Silliman's request to write up his own experiment on induction, before the details of Faraday's experiments were known here, a great public hullabaloo was raised against him for not telling about his discovery earlier. It seemed that no one stopped to compare their positions—unknown Joseph Henry, the poor high-school teacher, and famous Michael Faraday with his Royal Institution and subsidy from the Crown, discovering the same law of physics. It was a bitter experience. From that time on Joseph never once laid claim to being the discoverer of induction. He always mentioned Faraday in connection with it. And he had a sorrow now of a private kind that helped etch more sad lines on his big, bluff face. The great cholera epidemic of 1832 swept up the Hudson River valley from New York, and although he and Harriet moved with the rest of the family out to Galway, they were too late. Their little baby died, their first-born. Harriet, always so ready with sympathy and consolation, so tender-hearted, seemed to feel grief more than others. Their friends, Dr. Philip Ten-Eyck, Joseph's assistant; Harriet's brother, Stephen; Dr. Beck; William Dunlap, his friend from his theatrical days, all tried to cheer them up. And others, friends who knew them only by their acts, helped, too.

When the first cold weather put a stop to the epidemic Joseph had a new job and a new home. Everything had seemed so dark and hopeless, with the whole ambition of his life turned to wind and wishes. Then came a letter offering him the position of professor of natural philosophy at the College of New Jersey at Princeton. The salary was a thousand dollars a year and, if all went well at the end of the year he would get a raise to fifteen hundred and a house would be furnished him on the campus. Here he could pursue the life of a scientist in surroundings conducive to thought and growth, in the company of men who spoke the language of reason and investigation that is the savant's working tool.

He left Harriet, pregnant, at her mother's house in Albany and went to Princeton. It was early November, and the trees that he came to be so fond of were bare and black against the steely sky and the cold stone buildings. Inside, all was cheerful hospitality. The smiles, the warm handshakes, the steaming teacups, the friendly conversation, the popping, crackling cannel-coal fire exploding bursts of ruddy light on the cordial scene, all found Joseph Henry so humbly, so sincerely happy to be welcome here. He had, by his own efforts, much of it while alone and pinched for time and money, worked to make this happen. He had thought he had lost all chance of it, because he had not dared enough. A little nervous twitch in his upper lip went away. "My whole ambition is to establish for myself *and to deserve* the reputation of a man of science." [8]

No doubt it never occurred to him that the people at Princeton might have been relieved to find him so simple, friendly, and unpretentious.

His lecture room was upstairs in Philosophical Hall, a building long since torn down. This was a large room with seats in the center for the students and glass-fronted cases all around the walls to hold equipment for experiments. In a projection off the back of the building was another room, medium-sized, and two smaller ones for his use. Prominently displayed was a sign reading, *A place for everything and everything in its place,* over a coiled whip—meant humorously, returning the equipment being the best part of a

73

physics class. And, of course, there one could see the first true electromagnet, which he had brought with him from Albany.

He would dictate a synopsis of the material to be covered during the class period to his assistant, who would write it on a blackboard for the class to copy. After the laboratory work was over each student was supposed to write up the experiments, using this synopsis as a guide. During the first year he taught at Princeton he did no original experiments because planning his course of lectures took all his time. When the next academic year started he had his raise, his fine big house, and the assurance of success. Harriet and the new baby were proudly ensconced in their new home. He was unable, however, to get started on a new series of experiments this year because he took over Dr. Torrey's classes in chemistry, mineralogy, and geology in addition to his own, so that the eminent geologist could go to Europe. He enjoyed teaching and approached each class with interest and vigor, not like some of his colleagues, who nervously read their notes to a bored group of students and thankfully vanished back into their private world of research. He felt it the duty of a college teacher to instruct not only in the subject matter but also to give a strict indoctrination in inductive reasoning. His students rapidly learned not to start with the assumption of a fact and then look for proofs to back it up. They assembled all the facts they could and then drew a conclusion from them.

With a happy faculty for making friends, this year Henry outdid himself. He met Alexander Dallas Bache, and it was as if both had suddenly found some hitherto-missing part of themselves and become in each other's company a complete person. Bache was Benjamin Franklin's great-grandson, and at this time professor of natural philosophy at the University of Pennsylvania. His wife, the former Nancy Fowler of Rhode Island, was tiny, quick-witted, and since she came from an impeccable family, was in a position to scorn social conventions and be thought only eccentric, not vulgar. One of her innocent peculiarities was to have the drawing-room windows full of house plants, and curtainless.

Before the Henrys concluded that Princeton was heaven on earth as far as they were concerned, however, their second child died. Harriet began to worry for fear that she would never have a child live long enough for her to see it grown. She clucked and fussed over Joseph until he was completely spoiled, which seemingly gave them both great satisfaction.

Joseph started working on his electrical experiments again, building an electromagnet for Princeton that would lift 3,500 pounds. He invented the transformer (with rare justice beating out Faraday in publishing) and discovered self-induction so far ahead of everyone else that he was actually to have the pleasure of explaining one phase of it to Faraday in person, as well as to Wheatstone and Daniell, other famous British electrical scientists.

In 1837, as a reward for the hard work he had done, Henry was given a year's leave on full pay so that he could tour Europe and meet the world's famous scientists in person. It was a fine thing for him, and it was a fine thing for this country to have representing it this man with the unsophisticated and stainless integrity, the simple religious trust of a child, the dislike of foul talk and practical jokes. He was striking-looking, so big and blond, his square face always clean-shaven, with those sad, wise eyes and that marvelous bearing of his. Many years later a friend summed up the strange, winning way he had as a "quiet liveliness," [9] which seems a fair description of that kind of personality which charms without effort.

Harriet knew she had to stay home. It was her own choice

and one she was happy with. Joseph would be talking about
his trip to Europe for years; she would have it memorized
in time, so it would never be something that she did without
entirely. They had a third child now, a fine, healthy boy
named William Alexander, for her to stay home and take
care of. Having lost the two earlier ones, she would take no
chances of any sort. Joseph and Harriet each had something
that they were very happy about in 1837, and if experienced
apart, there would be years in which to share it all with each
other.

Lonely on the Salisbury plain, the naked monoliths of
Stonehenge showed pale and unreal in the moonlight. The
silence of where man has been and is no more rang in Joseph's eager American ears. There was feeling there, overwhelming, of ages and ages of time gone by that nothing
yet discovered in his country had. His romantic nature was
so entranced he could almost see the Druids' rituals.[10] Re-
luctantly he went back to the coach waiting to take him to
London and rode on, lost in dreams.

In London he met Faraday and other prominent British
scientists; each of them, properly impressed by the big
American, was fairly worshiped in return (Henry could
hardly feel secure in a national pride when he felt uncom-
fortably that he might be it). He met the Baches, who were
also seeing Europe and, being childless, were not tied down
as one of the Henrys had to be. They went to the theater
to see Forest in *Macbeth*, visited the Tower of London and
the museums like standard tourists, and met the important
people. Joseph couldn't get over the dirtiness of the town.
These people came to his raw, new country and sneered at
it because it was ugly! Here in their own country coal smoke
had turned the great buildings gray. It drifted sooty streaks

and heaps about the streets and walks and left dark stains when the frequent showers failed to wash it away. There were so many beggars, so many ragged, filthy, hopeless-looking children. He even failed to be impressed by the famous Bull and Mouth Inn, with its many-windowed concave front facing on Regent Circus,[11] where he was staying.

Things were not going well back home, there was a financial panic and a severe depression, with mobs breaking into warehouses in New York, but nothing Henry had ever seen compared with Paris. Here were not only dirt and a great deal more poverty and suffering, but also such a thorough richness of stenches that it was obviously a long-accepted condition. And, showing off in their fine open carriages, rode the richly dressed new aristocracy who apparently were unmoved by what they saw on the raw boulevards. He did plenty of sight-seeing here, but Joseph Henry was more impressed by Guy-Lussac's solid block of carbonic acid than anything else he saw in Paris. This was so cold that it would burn a person's hand if held only seconds, and froze fifteen pounds of mercury in less than a minute.

Back in London he was annoyed to find the slavery question rampant. He explained that in New York they had prohibited slavery in 1817 and given slaveowners ten years to dispose of their human property and that no one there owned slaves now; slavery had been outlawed on British soil only five years before. But, his British friends protested, there were still slaveowning states in America. Henry explained that no state could tell another how to run its business; it all had to be done through Congress. "Gag rule" had come along to cloud the issue, the abolitionists claiming that, since they were not allowed to petition against slavery in Congress, freedom was truly dead. The British argued that in favoring slavery thus the federal government actually encouraged it.

Joseph was glad to escape to Scotland, where the spirit of Sir Walter Scott still colored the misty hills and gray towns with a romance that called to the ex-Hendrie's tribal emotions. He saw Abbotsford, and tall Holyrood standing over Edinburgh, and ruins of castles and dark forests and lonely shielings where the kilt might yet be seen. He also visited more prominent scientists and heard the story going around about that crazy fellow, Smithson his name was, one of the Northumberland bastards,[12] who had left a hundred thousand pounds to found some institution of learning in the United States. Little could come of it; it was just an oddity in the news.

Back at Princeton he plunged into his work, devising a multitude of new experiments. Not content with wiring the laboratory, he strung wire all around the campus, even to his house, and used it for sending messages by a private code. He was busy, engrossed, and happy:

I think the first actual line of telegraph using the earth as a conductor was made in the beginning of 1836. A wire was extended across the front campus of the college grounds, from the upper story of the library building to the philosophical hall on the opposite side, the ends terminating in two wells. Through this wire, signals were sent from my house to my laboratory. The electro-magnetic telegraph was first invented by me, in Albany, in 1830. Professor Morse, according to his statements, conceived the idea of an electromagnetic telegraph in his voyage across the ocean in 1832 but did not until several years afterward—1837—attempt to carry his ideas into practice; and when he did so, he found himself so little acquainted with the subject of electricity that he could not make his simple machine operate through the distance of a few yards. In this dilemma he called in the aid of Dr. Leonard D. Gale, who was well acquainted with what I had done in Albany and Princeton, having visited me in the latter place. He informed Professor Morse that he had not the right kind of a battery nor the right kind of magnets, whereupon the professor turned the matter over to him, and, with the knowledge he had obtained from my researches, he was enabled to make the instrument work through a distance of several miles. At the time of making my original experiments on electro-magnetism in Albany, I was urged by a friend to take out a patent, both for its application to machinery and to the telegraph, but this I declined, on the ground that I did not then consider it compatible with the dignity of science to confine the benefits which might be derived from it to the exclusive use of any individual. In this perhaps I was too fastidious.

To Mr. Morse great credit is due for his alphabet [code], and for his perseverance in bringing the telegraph into practical use.

Mr. Faraday had discovered that when a current of galvanic electricity was passed through a wire from a battery, a current in an opposite direction was induced in a wire arranged parallel to this conductor. I discovered that an induction of a similar kind took place in the primary conducting wire itself, so that a current which, in its passage through a short wire conductor, would neither produce sparks nor shocks, would, if the wire were sufficiently long, produce both these phenomena. The effect was most strikingly exhibited when the conductor was a flat ribbon, covered with silk, rolled into the form of a helix. With this, brilliant deflagrations and other electrical effects of high intensity were produced by means of a current from a battery of low intensity, such as that of a single element.

Another series of investigations was made in regard to ordinary or frictional electricity. In the course of these it was shown that effects could be produced by it at a remarkable distance. For example, if a shock were sent through a wire on the outside of a building, electrical effects could be exhibited in a parallel wire within the building. As another illustration of this, it may be mentioned that when a discharge of a battery of several Leyden jars was sent through the wire before mentioned, stretched across the campus in front of Nassau Hall, an inductive effect was produced in a parallel wire, the ends of which terminated in the plates of metal in the ground in the back campus, at a distance of several hundred feet from the primary current, the building of Nassau Hall intervening.

The discharge of electricity from a Leyden jar is of an oscillatory character, a principal discharge taking place in one direction, and immediately afterward a rebound in the opposite, and so on forward and backward, until the equilibrium is obtained.

The next series of experiments was on the induction from thunder clouds. For this purpose the tin covering of the roof of the house in which I resided was used as an inductive plate. A wire was soldered to the edge of the roof near the gutter, was passed into my study and out again through holes in the window-sash, and terminated in connection with a plate of metal in a deep well immediately in front of the house. By breaking the continuity of that part of the wire which was in the study, and introducing into the opening a magnetizing spiral, needles placed in this could be magnetized by a flash of lightning so distant that the thunder could scarcely be heard. The electrical disturbance produced in this case was also found to be of an oscillatory character, a discharge first passing through the wire from the roof to the well, then another in the opposite direction.

In connection with this class of investigations a series of experiments was made in regard to lightning-rods. It was found that when a quantity of electricity was thrown upon a rod, the lower end of which was connected with a plate of metal sunk in the water of a deep well, that the electricity did not descend silently into water, but that sparks could be drawn from every part of the rod sufficiently intense to explode an electrical pistol and to set fire to delicate inflammable substances. The spark thus given off was found to be of a peculiar character, for while it produced combustion and gave a slight shock, and fired the electrical pistol, it scarcely affected a gold-leaf electroscope. Indeed, it consisted of two sparks, one from the conductor and another to it, in such rapid succession that the rupture of the air by the first served for the path of the second. The conclusion arrived at was, that during the passage of the electricity down the rod each point in succession received a charge analogous to the statical charge of a prime conductor, and that this charge, in its passage down the rod, was immediately preceded by a negative charge; the two in their passage past the point at which the spark was drawn giving rise to its duplex character. It was also shown by a series of experiments in transmitting a powerful discharge through a portion of air, that the latter, along the path of discharge, was endowed for a moment with an intense repulsive energy. So great is this that in one instance, when an electrical discharge from the clouds passed between two chimneys through the cockloft of a house, the whole roof was lifted from the walls. It is to this repulsive energy, or tendency in air to expand at right angles to the path of a stroke of lightning that the mechanical effects which accompany the latter are generally to be attributed.

Another series of investigations was on the phosphorogenic emanation from the sun. . . .

The next series of investigations was on a method of determining the velocity of projectiles. . . .

Another series of experiments was in regard to the relative heat of different parts of the sun's disk, and especially to that of the spots on the surface. These were made in connection with Professor S. Alexander, and consisted in throwing an image of the sun on a screen in a dark room by drawing out the eye-piece of a telescope. Through a hole in the screen the end of a sensitive thermopile was projected, the wires of which were connected with a galvanometer. By slightly moving the smaller end of the telescope, different parts of the image of the sun could be thrown on the end of the thermopile, and by the deviation of the needle of the galvanometer, the variation of the heat was indicated. In this way it was proved that the spots radiated less heat than the adjacent parts, and that all parts of the sun's surface did not give off an equal amount of heat.

Another series of experiments was made with what was called a thermal telescope. This instrument consisted of a long, hollow cone of pasteboard, lined with silver leaf and painted outside with lampblack. The angle at the apex of this cone was such as to cause all the parallel rays from a distant object entering the larger end of the cone to be reflected on to the end of a thermopile, the poles of which were connected with a delicate galvanometer. When the axis of this conical reflector was directed toward a distant object of greater or less temperature than the surrounding bodies, the difference was immediately indicated by the deviation of the needle of the galvanometer. For example, when the object was a horse in a distant field, the radiant heat from the animal was distinctly perceptible at a distance of at least several hundred yards. When this instrument was turned toward the celestial vault, the radiant heat was observed to increase from the zenith downward; when directed, however, to different clouds, it was found to indicate in some cases a greater, and in others a less, degree of radiation than the surrounding space. When the same instrument was directed to the moon, a slight increase of temperature was observed over that of the adjacent sky, but this increase of heat was attributed to the reflection of the heat of the sun from the surface of the moon and not to the heat of the moon itself.

Another series of experiments had their origin in the examination of the large gun constructed under the direction of Captain Stockton, by the explosion of which several prominent members of the United States Government were killed at Washington. It was observed in testing the bars of iron made from this gun that they varied much in tensile strength in different parts and that in breaking these bars the solution of the continuity took place first in the interior. This phenomenon was attributed to the more ready mobility

of the outer molecules of the bars, the inner ones being surrounded by matter incapable of slipping, and hence the rupture.

In 1846, while still at Princeton, I was requested by members of the Board of Regents of the Smithsonian Institution,
which was then just founded, to study the will of Smithson,
and to give a plan of organization by which the object of
the bequest might be realized. My conclusion was that the
intention of the donor was to advance science by original
research and publication, that the establishment was for
the benefit of mankind generally, and that all unnecessary
expenditures on local objects would be violations of the
trust. The plan I proposed for the organization of the Institution was to assist men of science in making original
researches, to publish these in a series of volumes, and to give
a copy to every first-class library on the face of the earth.[13]

In after years he was to refer to his stay on the Princeton
campus as the happiest years of his life. Here were born his
three daughters, Mary, Helen (Nell), and Caroline (Carrie). They were a close, happy family, with many friends.
Harriet's brother Stephen had taken a job as professor of
mathematics and astronomy at Princeton and they were always in and out of each other's homes. Joseph's initial taste
in English literature had grown to include Shakespeare, the
great English poets, and popular ones not so great, and an
unquenchable fondness for Sir Walter Scott. In the classic
tradition of education he was exposed to much of the good
of the ancient Greek civilization and it was always a pet field
of his. He was fond also of attending sporting events at the
college, and would often marvel at how involved emotionally
he would get in wanting someone to win who seemed to be
trying extra hard. They were unusual people. Joseph was
as wholeheartedly sympathetic as Harriet was charitable.
In April of 1842 they even took into their home a student
ill with typhus who had no one to care for him.[14]

Joseph's interest in the Morse telegraph was most sincerely benevolent, with no idea on his part of ever making a cent from his relays and electromagnets, which were indespensable parts of it. That there would come a day when Morse would turn against him he had no slightest idea. He had heard Dr. Gale's story of the way Morse had given up everything in order to perfect his telegraphic apparatus and felt great sympathy toward the painter-inventor in his struggles. He wrote Morse at least one letter of encouragement, complimenting him on his efforts.

In late 1843 his friend Bache took over as head of the Coast Survey following the death of Ferdinand Hassler, its Swiss-born founder, and moved to Washington. Bache must have felt over his head in the Washington political swamp, a far call from his duties as an educator. But the great-grandson of Ben Franklin was determined to be better at his job than men who had worked for years as surveyors and cartographers and who felt one of them should have been chosen for the position. He perfected measuring instruments, spent every summer in the field with surveying parties, and took a special interest in sending ships out to investigate the Gulf Stream that had fascinated his great-grandfather. He so charmed the Swiss naturalist Louis Agassiz with his invitation to use Coast Survey boats while doing his research on coral reefs in Florida that Agassiz became an American citizen. Still not caring for Washington and longing for more civilized surroundings, Bache began to search for ways to get those friends whose companionship he missed to come to the capital.

Many of Henry's researches were now so far ahead of his own understanding and that of his contemporaries that it would seem about time for him to stop and let the field of electronics catch up with him. In one of the experiments he wrote up he was actually sending out and receiving Hertzian

waves fifty years before Herr Hertz discovered them. He
even understood that it was some kind of wave phenomenon
in that he compared it with "that of a spark from a flint and
steel in the case of light." But it was too immense a field to
conquer at this time.

The Mexican War came and went almost unnoticed, so
absorbed was he in his speculations and in his projects for
carrying out those speculations as logical demonstrations.
He published thirteen technical papers in 1845 and 1846,
on every subject from the aurora borealis to color blindness
and including much on a pet problem of his, lightning damage.

In September of 1846 Bache's young brother, George
Meade Bache, was lost at sea, washed overboard during a
hurricane off Nag's Head. He had been out on a cruise
through the Gulf Stream on the survey brig *Washington*,
and had lost the race for port with the storm. He had been
a virtual son to his childless brother and sister-in-law.

With his great love for Bache, and his warm, sympathetic
nature, Henry was extremely loath now to hurt him more.
Bache was trying to get a job for him in Washington. Henry
was happy in his research and teaching, and it would mean
great sacrifice for him to accept this position, although it
was offered to him in the most flattering way possible, by a
vote of Congress. It meant a lot more money. In fact, it
meant getting the Smithsonian Institution started. Half a
million dollars at his disposal, "To found at Washington,
under the name of the Smithsonian Institution, an establishment for the increase and diffusion of knowledge among
men," or so read Smithson's will. Everyone liked Henry's
plan, Bache had gotten a surprising number of scientists,
both foreign and domestic, to write that he was the leading
American scientist, and the whole thing was practically
forced on him.

The last of 1846 found Joseph Henry and his family in Washington, living across the street from the Patent Office in a large rooming house at Eighth and G, NW.

NOTES TO CHAPTER FIVE

1. *Joseph Henry, His Life and Works*, Coulson.
2. *A Mirror for Americans*, ed. Tryon.
3. Asa Gray, the Harvard botanist and friend of Henry, in *Joseph Henry, A Memorial*.
4. There is not supposed to be a known picture of Mrs. Henry. However, Coulson prints a picture of a meeting of the National Academy of Sciences in the Smithsonian in which one of the women is identified as Mary Henry. Three seats away is another woman, older, who is Mary's absolute double. This is too much to put down to coincidence, since they are facing the camera at the same angle. There are only half-a-dozen women present and the rest are outrageous old hags. And since Mary doesn't look like her father—Q.E.D., she looks like her mother, there present with her.
5. *Joseph Henry, A Memorial*, page 174.
6. What he did was lift the rack of battery plates out of the acid and dip them back in again.
7. *Joseph Henry, A Memorial*, page 492.
8. *Joseph Henry, A Memorial*, page 60. Also the bit of business about his upper lip twitching is from the same work, one of his former students reminiscing about Henry as a professor at Princeton.
9. Jefferson Davis, no less; quoted in *Alexander Dallas Bache*, by Odgers.
10. You and I may know Stonehenge was pre-Druidic, but Joseph Henry didn't.
11. From a John Moore print dated 1829 in the author's possession: "The Age, Brighton Coach at the Bull and Mouth, Regent Circus, Piccadilly."

12. We regret to say this is no figure of speech.

13. *Joseph Henry, A Memorial.* Actually this is a synopsis of a letter written to the Reverend S. B. Dod on December 4, 1876, about sixteen printed pages.

14. Letter to his brother James, no date other than April 1842.

CHAPTER SIX

Maury on Ships and Stars

THE SAILING SHIP had been around for about five thousand years [1] when it reached its zenith as a thing of beauty and usefulness in the American clipper. When the clipper went, sailing went. And with the clipper went American merchant shipping, hurried along by Matthew Fontaine Maury to both perfection and destruction.

Great Britain and the United States engaged in a great struggle for the lion's share of sea trade after the War of 1812. Many British ships had been destroyed by our privateers during the war, and now those privateers, refitted as merchantmen, were out to snatch away the cargoes from the remaining British ships. We had great forests and many men trained in the shipbuilding trades, even the British used our sails, our ropewalks were the finest in the world, and our ship designers as bold and daring as the ship captains. We concentrated on speed. Also, tradition did not weigh us down as it did older countries, and we were able to progress more rapidly through the morass of things-that-weren't-done.

Take the matter of sailing schedules. Prior to 10:00 A.M., January 5, 1818, when the Black Ball line's *James Monroe* sailed from New York to Liverpool "as advertised," there were no schedules. Ships customarily sailed when their cargo space was filled. That was one of those simple things that "everybody" knew—and knocking it on the head was the first step toward our rule of the merchant sea lanes. Shippers could depend on our ships sailing when the advertisements in the papers said they would, and cargoes were delivered as fast as wind, currents, and captains such as "Kicking Jack" Williams could drive them. These were the packet ships—the term "packet" referring not to their build, which was that of any large, three-masted ship, but to their schedules and speed. The first-class "saloons" and cabins were fitted up like rooms in luxury resorts, with satinwood paneling and rosewood furniture, and they featured bills of fare that were needlessly ostentatious. Westbound passages were apt to be faintly smelly, however, since below, in the steerage, would be crowded from five hundred to eight hundred immigrants, furnished only with stoves and water. Still, the *Red Jacket* was thirteen and a half days, New York to Liverpool, better than many a freighter of today.

Most famed of the packets was the *Dreadnought*, Captain Samuels. It had a red cross sewn on the top foresail, since it was owned by the St. George's Cross Line, and was deep-hulled and full-rigged. It still holds the transatlantic sailing record. It was built to sail best in the bad weather that is so common in the North Atlantic, and when other ships had turned to ride out the storm, the *Dreadnought*, nose down, driven to the limit, plowed on across the rough seas. In one twenty-four-hour period she made 320 miles easting, and 400-horsepower side-wheelers meekly got themselves out of her way.

They still sing about the Dreadnought:

Maury on Ships and Stars

Oh, there's a crack packet that's well-known to fame,
She comes from New York and the Dreadnought's *her name.*
You may speak of your packets, Swallow Tail *and* Black Ball,
But the Dreadnought's *the flier that will beat them all.*

The Dreadnought *is waiting in the river Mersey,*
She waits for the tugboat to take her to sea,
And when she's off soundings you shortly will know
She's the Liverpool packet, oh, Lord, let 'er go.

Oh, the Dreadnought's *a-bowling down the wild Irish Sea,*
Her passengers merry, their hearts full of glee,
And her sailors like tigers walk the decks to and fro,
She's the Liverpool packet, oh, Lord, let 'er go.

Oh, the Dreadnought's *howling 'cross the Atlantic so wide,*
While the rough seas do roll past her black-painted side,
And her sails are all spread so the Red Cross will show
She's the Liverpool packet, oh, Lord, let 'er go.

The Dreadnought's *becalmed on the Banks of Newfoundland*
Where the water is shallow and the bottom is sand;
Say all the little fishes that swim to and fro—
She's the Liverpool packet, oh, Lord, let 'er go.

Immense crews were needed to sail these ships because of their quantities of canvas and the way in which they were rigged. It was uneconomical to operate packet ships in a decent, civilized manner, so the most unfortunate fellows of the seaports, the witless, the drunken, the unlucky, were shanghaied aboard to join a skeleton crew of masochists and be beaten by bucko mates into a force capable of handling the ship. They were known as packet rats, fighting words in seaports around the world, and made about eight dollars a month.

John W. Griffiths and Donald McKay were busy designing a new kind of ship, sharply raked, her bow incurved so that to the old sailor it seemed turned inside out, her widest part amidships, her bow undercut. Onto this slender slipper of a ship they put the tallest masts she could carry without capsizing when loaded with full sails. This was the clipper ship.

Clipper ships did perfectly what they had been designed to do. They sailed. They batted along in monsoons close hauled, they ghosted through dead calms when the packets stood like mulish boys with their hands in their pockets, refusing to budge. They raced to China and back again, making five trips to every four made by the British barks. They were beautiful to behold, too.

The *Flying Cloud*, Captain Josiah P. Cressy, was the most famous of the clipper ships. She was 208 feet long on the keel, 229 on deck, 40 feet wide, had a registered tonnage of 1,783, and carried 13,000 running yards of canvas. For beauty, seaworthiness, and speed, she was never to be equaled. Her maiden voyage she was 89 days out, New York to San Francisco, on a run that took 133 days for the average ship.

But it was not by Yankee ingenuity alone that our packets and clippers, our whaling ships and fishing schooners, too, were able to go so fast and be handled so wisely despite the whims of the sea. Our Virginia-Tennessee sailor, though landlocked now, had as much a part in forming our superiority on the sea as daring shipbuilders, tough captains, and composers of sea chanteys. In a way, it was Maury's ocean.

In a way, it is still Maury's ocean.

Into a double house at 2422–2424 Pennsylvania Avenue [2] in Washington City, Maury moved the Depot of Charts and Instruments. There weren't so many charts and instruments, but the law required that logbooks of all ships of the United States Navy be kept for a certain number of years, and there were more than aplenty of those useless things. There were meteorological equipment, a lithographic press for printing their own charts, and a number of second-rate telescopes that had been furnished so the chronometers could be set by sidereal or star time. With so many playthings Mat could hardly decide what to concentrate on. So he didn't. He worked from eight or nine in the morning until one or two at night just to be sure he didn't miss anything. Despite later protestations that he knew nothing about astronomy, his letters of this period are full of references to star gazing and how beautiful some of the double stars were; of course, he had used the Wilkes Expedition astronomical equipment in Philadelphia in 1837.

He wrote his cousin Ann that his doctor had told him he was killing himself with overwork on February 16, 1843. For a year all his letters carried the protest that he had no brains left or that they had gone on strike. He had added editing the *Southern Literary Messenger* to his already heavy load. He was supervising preparation of a chart of the Atlantic at the Depot, carrying on astronomical observations, making speeches, and doing his regular work, too. Also—Congress had appropriated $35,000 for the construction of a regular observatory, which was now being built and superintendency of which Mat was angling for.

But he kept coming back again and again to the logbooks. There were so many of them, dirty, splotched with mildew, still smelling of the sea, and they had so many entries, all gone to waste now. Limping, cane in hand, around the cramped quarters into which he had moved his family recently, he could feel the thousands of stories those books had in them, stories of storms and currents and winds at sea. If he could only put those stories together, maybe they would tell him a lot about the winds and currents that no one else knew anything about!

The whole Depot was shaken to its roots. His assistant, his brother-in-law, Lewis Herndon, and many a confused reefer were put to work compiling the information in those logbooks. In a little while—it was amazing how fast this information accumulated once they decided on a form to put it in—they could tell what winds prevailed at certain times of the year in five-degree areas of the North Atlantic, and where those currents' true routes were that wandered about the oceans. It was, it seemed to Maury, as if the logbooks were a quarry from which they mined the form of the ocean's winds, currents, weather, and something very like sensible paths for ships to follow going to certain places.

At the beginning of this decade of the great ships of America it took 180 days to sail from New York to San Francisco. Maury's charts were to cut their time to 130 days, unless you took passage on the *Andrew Jackson* out to break the record of the *Flying Cloud* (it tied it), in which case the old time was cut in half! That was one sample of the utility of Maury's work.

None of the previous Depot heads had thought to utilize the raw material in the logbooks, possibly because they were all astronomers of one cut or another, more interested in navigation by the sun and stars and in theories of such than in the actual sailing of a ship. Mat had never been impressed by astronomy as the sacred and mighty clock in the sky that timed all things. He figured that it was an instrument of God and no more important than any other of His works. But this was the age of invention: he was important who was first; and Mat knew he had found a vast field to "first" in. It gave him great satisfaction to know that Charles Wilkes, recently court-martialed and reprimanded for cruelty to his

crew following the return of the Exploring Expedition after
four years at sea, once had those logbooks under his jurisdiction and had failed to see anything in them. Certainly some
of the foremost navy scientists had been responsible for
storing the logbooks. Lieutenant L. M. Goldsborough had
founded the Depot of Charts and Instruments in 1830 as a
needed place to store charts, chronometers, and other valuable items. Wilkes had built the first observatory at his
own expense, using a three-and-three-fourths-inch transit
instrument loaned by the Coast Survey. However, he had
done no observing. He was interested only in the clock in
the sky by which to rate his chronometers. When Wilkes was
sent to England in 1836 to collect equipment for the Exploring Expedition, Lieutenant James M. Gilliss was put in
charge. He was an astronomer and began the first regular
observations, cataloging more than twelve hundred stars
and procuring much needed equipment. Of course the Navy's
need for an exact-time criterion, by which the rate of gain
or loss of their valuable navigational chronometers was figured, was never far behind in his consideration.

When Maury took over the Depot in the summer of 1842,
Gilliss was sent to Europe to buy instruments for the new
observatory. This observatory (this $35,000 observatory!)
was being built on a high-lying plot of government-owned
land out where the Potomac inlet to the town ditch was located, one of the unhealthiest spots in an unhealthy town.
Lieutenant Gilliss was also in charge of the construction of
the observatory and everyone thought he would be its first
superintendent, since he was so hard working and well liked.
But down at the Depot there was Lieutenant Maury, looking at the telescopes, the meridian circle, the transit, the
sidereal clock, and the mean-time clock, as well as tending
to the stores of instruments and the progress of their chart
publication, and to the business of keeping in well with the

Virginian and later the Tennesseean in the White House.

For some time now things had been going badly with the Navy. The *Somers* mutiny had resulted in a large-sized scandal, and the Navy had forbidden any officer or seaman to mention the affair under pain of court-martial. If they could have gag rule in Congress they could have it in the Navy. Especially since one of the too-quickly-hanged mutineers was a nineteen-year-old midshipman named Philip Spencer, whose father had been Secretary of War in 1841 and who was, in short order, appointed Secretary of the Treasury. Hardly had this affair dimmed in the public memory than the new steam frigate *Missouri* was totally destroyed by fire while at anchor at Gibraltar. Reason: naval brass had refused to order storage of inflammable liquids in metal containers, and a butter-fingered yeoman dropped a jar full of turpentine inopportunely. Then the *Princeton* disaster came along. Captain Robert Stockton had met John Ericsson, the inventor of the screw propeller,[3] while in England, and pursuaded him to come to America. Secretary of the Navy Upshur got Ericsson to build a steam-propelled ship without the cumbersome paddle wheels which one shot could disable, and also to design a new twelve-inch gun. On February 28, 1844, the Navy made a gala day excursion from Washington to show off this new *Princeton*. Guests were everyone that counted, from President Tyler on down. Despite Ericsson's protests that it was unsafe, a new gun invented by Captain Stockton was also taken along for trial. The *Princeton* was loaded with newfangled devices and doodads—in fact, the engine was so fearful and wonderful that no second one was ever attempted—and everyone was exclaiming at the wonder of it all. Ericsson's gun was fired successfully. Stockton's gun was fired and blew to bits, killing Abel Upshur, just appointed Secretary of State, and

96

the new Secretary of the Navy, Thomas Gilmer, a couple of congressmen, and one of the ship's officers, and wounded Stockton and twelve others.

Citizens were starting to wonder if the Navy was run by imbeciles. Something constructive had to be done. The Naval Observatory was being rushed to completion. It was necessary to put someone in charge of it who would reflect credit on the Navy. Lieutenant Gilliss was one of the most popular hosts in town, his large family entertained often and pleasantly, and everyone liked him. However, he lacked that drive, that ambition, that self-seeking singleness of purpose that make men known. He was happy to be an unknown astronomer, doing accurate work and enjoying it.

While the observatory was still under construction Mat Maury had been keeping himself in the public eye. He made a most entertaining speech on the Gulf Stream to a company composed of President Tyler and the diplomatic corps and honored guests. He devised blank charts to be used by sea captains to show, day by day, their positions, the weather, currents, etc., and spoke on it before the National Institute. He worked with the old taxometer and tried to get top naval figures to have it installed as navigational equipment on Navy ships, which met with as much success as it deserved, and worked continually at his writing. He revised *Maury on Navigation*. And to all this was added the fact that the current Secretary of the Navy was that eminent Virginian, John Y. Mason.

On October 1, 1844, the keys of the new Naval Observatory, then called the National Observatory, were turned over to Lieutenant Maury. Assisted by Lieutenants William Lewis Herndon, B. F. Sands, and G. H. Scott, and by Passed Midshipmen J. L. Worden, R. H. Getty, J. M. B. Clitz, J. F. Stenson, and W. B. Fitzgerald, Mat got the Depot's charts and instruments moved out to the Observatory. The old instruments and clocks were set up and the new equipment was unpacked.

Mat's mysterious illness vanished. The new 9½-inch equatorial was to him a thing of beauty and wonder. When we read his enthusiastic description of a star "dancing" into his field of vision we can only wonder what his reaction would have been had he had then the 26-inch Clarke refractor that was installed in 1873 and with which Professor Asaph Hall discovered the moons of Mars. Perhaps it would have made an astronomer out of him. Perhaps it would have produced more than the brief enthusiasm which he gloried in, and then abandoned with such vindictive finality. However, for a few years his name was placed more or less regularly on the lists of observers. Using the 9½-inch refractor, one of his staff, Mr. Ferguson, discovered "for the Navy" the asteroids Euphrosyne, Echo, and Virginia. By order of Secretary of the Navy Bancroft, the staff was engaged in cataloging all the stars they could observe at that latitude. While they didn't actually discover Neptune, their observations of where Lalande erroneously had charted it as a fixed star helped to determine its orbit after Leverrier's discovery. Yarnall, Walker, Hubbard, some of the professors who did most of the observing, are notable names in the field of astronomy. They published three volumes of stellar observations, for the years 1847, 1848, and 1849–50. Gilliss's catalog, published in 1846, based on his observations with the old equipment, was the first star catalog published concerning work by a regular observatory in the United States.

Carried away by its success with the Observatory, the Navy began to look for further ways to improve.

The new President, James K. Polk of Tennessee, inaugurated amid threats of impending war with Mexico, put the historian George Bancroft in charge of the Navy. Bancroft, who believed in licking trouble before it started, founded the naval school. It having proved impossible to get the bill through a Congress that hated all forms of aristocracy and was trying to get the Army school at West Point abolished, Bancroft had to sneak a school into operation. With old Fort Severn borrowed from the Army, some odds and ends of naval funds marked for instruction purposes, and what reputable professors the Navy could command, a school was started. Mids were pulled off vessels, where they were little pests learning by osmosis how to run a ship, and enrolled, often despite the most vehement protests. Maury's long-standing efforts to get a naval academy started gave him cause for pleasant reflections now.

The first wind and current chart was issued under Maury's direction in 1847. Nothing like it ever had been seen before. It was handed out free to all sea captains who offered to report certain requested information on wind, tides, etc., and it was made obligatory for captains of ships of the United States Navy to complete this information on a pre-scribed form for each cruise. Mat even reported Captains Stribling and Buchanan for failing to record this log in-formation. The first chart grew into a regular series of six: Track Charts, Trade-wind Charts, Pilot Charts, Whale Charts, Thermal Charts, and Wind and Rain Charts. As time passed eight editions of *Sailing Directions* were issued to accompany this series of so-called Wind and Current Charts.

The navies and commercial fleets of the whole world saw that here was indeed something. Weeks and days were knocked off the usual runs of sailing ships. Many millions of dollars were saved by the information in these charts and sailing directions. There were more than three hundred fifty whaling vessels in New Bedford alone to benefit by these charts, particularly the Whale Charts. Even the British, who had turned largely to government-subsidized steamships, found that their ships saved time and fuel by not bucking the Gulf Stream when crossing the Atlantic to the west and taking advantage of it going east. Time after time Congress was petitioned to allow Lieutenant M. F. Maury, U.S.N., to accept an award from some foreign government. Needless to say, official Washington was very happy about this—all except the people who felt that they were made to look small because Maury was made to look so very big. The injured Gilliss had a friend named Jefferson Davis, and one named Alexander Dallas Bache, and one named Joseph Henry. Small items began to accumulate steadily on the minus side of Maury's success ledger, although it would be years yet before they showed up.

Life in the Maury household was lively and pleasant, because the world was pleased with Pa, a state of affairs that Pa felt was completely justified. Three more little Maurys now toddled about the premises: John Herndon, known to his father as Davy Jones and to the family as Johnny; Mary Herndon, called Tots by her father and Mollie by the family; and Eliza Hull, called Glum by her father. They had a large Newfoundland dog named Vendovi after the unfortunate native king kidnaped by Captain Wilkes during the Exploring Expedition, and were all, aunts, cousins, and other adopted kith and kin, settled in the new superintendent's house recently built at the Observatory. Mother and children shared the fun of star-gazing on the balmy spring nights when it wasn't overcast, and the older children were permitted to copy Pa's notes for his new book in their precise copperplate script. For a family outing they would hire an omnibus, pack a picnic lunch, and go off to Chain Bridge at the Little Falls of the Potomac. The babies would nap under the bridge, the older children would fish, and the elders would keep busy making sure no one fell in the narrow, deep, white-rushing channel close to the Virginia shore. Mat would sometimes forget his cane and even Big Nannie could be heard to express a favorable attitude toward these simple joys. Summers, as a rule, Mrs. Maury would take the children and visit in Fredericksburg or, failing this, go to some jolly, healthy farm close by the Great Falls of the Potomac, where the fevers that plagued Washington were not found. Pa was left alone at the Observatory, with his duty, the stars, and the ague.

"Mad Jack" Percival wrote Maury that his cousin John Minor was beginning to see the light, and that he had hopes of making a useful addition to the Navy out of him yet. His nephew Dabney was also gone. Mat seemingly was closer to Dabney than he was to his children; Dabney was almost ridiculously little, but he had a noble head crowned with a shock of blond curls, quite all the brains anyone needed, a wonderful sense of humor, and he had met fear and overcome it. He was now in Mexico with his regiment, and his uncle Mat was violent in maintaining that the Mexicans ought to be treated with the greatest harshness to teach them not to try to stand up to us. We wanted New Mexico and California and a Texas border down to the Rio Grande, and Mexico objected. Not only that, they were arrogant about it, suggesting that we keep out of their business. Since it seemed obvious that we would win, we could hardly wait to get involved in a shooting war with the Mexicans. Dabney got a musket ball in his arm at Cerro Gordo and was sent home covered with glory and bandages. His uncle tried to finagle a hero's welcome for him, and was enraged that General Frémont's scout, Kit Carson, got it instead.

After Manifest Destiny had been suitably saluted by a reordering of political frontiers, the attention of our country was focused on internal problems. Not with moderation, though; not with determination to achieve solutions by constructive measures and peaceable means. A stiff-necked attitude prevailed, noses were looked down, snide cleverness and vile sarcasm were applauded, and the number of those who were dedicated to outhating their neighbors steadily increased. To sneer and jeer became desirably fashionable. An alarming number of Americans seemed bent on mutual destruction.

The battered Mexicans might well have felt that they could have the last laugh.

By January of 1849 the news that there was gold from the grass roots down in California had burst over a country suddenly desperate for rapid transportation. One could cross the country by slow wagon train, with the possibility of losing one's hair to a Paiute—the quick way—or having it fall out as a result of alkali poisoning from Bitter Creek water. One could spend an equal number of months going by way of Cape Horn in fair style, not allowing for the perpetual storms of the Straits of Magellan. One could disembark at Aspinwall and cross the jungle-choked Isthmus of Panama and wait to see if a ship would take you off on the other side before yellow fever did. All in all, the ships had an edge. And now the Wind and Current Charts were in every captain's hand. It was nothing for one voyage to the gold fields to pay the entire construction cost of a McKay-built clipper, new from the yards in East Boston. The great square-rigged clippers were bound on *going*.

Maury's charts covered a large field. He was not invariably first in the matters covered in them, by any means, but of an important part he was the originator. The Track Charts as first issued were general charts of weather and prevailing winds for the more commonly-traveled areas of the ocean. Later this title was used for a more important project, laying out actual ship lanes, to do away with col-

102

lisions in mid ocean and to lay a way south of the ice lanes in spring when the big bergs came down from Greenland. The Trade Wind Charts delineated the areas of the trade winds at various seasons and also showed the doldrums. The Pilot Charts went into great detail on the winds prevalent all over the oceans, by the month. The Whale Charts showed where various types of whales had been reported over the years. The Thermal Charts showed the temperatures of the surface waters. The Storm and Rain Charts went into great detail on the weather history of every square of five degrees in all the charted waters.

The early charts were readily understandable once one made out what they said. They were difficult to read, especially where a vast number of individual tracks were shown simultaneously, each one marked with the wind direction every so often and the ship's name and the date of the abstract log from which the track was projected. By the inadequate artificial lights of the day, they would have been all but impossible to read. No doubt they were subject to much criticism on that score, because the later ones were presented with averages of several tracks and were less cluttered with minutiae. The complete set of charts, with the books of *Sailing Directions* which accompanied them, cost fifty dollars from E. C. and J. Biddle, the publishers, in Philadelphia. Copies of the North Atlantic Wind and Current Chart were still handed out free to skippers who turned in completed abstract logs.

While attending to the wind and current business, Maury persuaded a friendly Secretary of the Navy to let the Observatory have ships with which to sound the ocean floor, and it actually had three at one time. John Brooks's deep-sea sounding device did fairly well until Lord Kelvin's piano-wire one came along. Maury began to advocate the building of a railroad across the Isthmus of Panama and even suggested that canal routes be surveyed in different parts of Central America. Thinking that slavery was overpopulating the South, he put forth plans for opening up the entire basin of the Amazon River to commerce and proposed dumping the South's surplus Negroes there. Of course, he didn't put it that bluntly; he made it look as if he was doing the world a favor. He was full of plans for steamship lines and transcontinental railroads. When Cyrus Field sounded him out on the possibility of a submarine telegraph across the Atlantic he became one of its most enthusiastic supporters and sent Field a description of the submarine plateau upon which such a cable could be laid between Ireland and Newfoundland.

In 1853 he was sent as the American delegate to the first world conference on recording the weather at sea.[4] Americans' absorption with the weather has always been viewed with contempt by Europeans, who have only the vaguest idea of what real weather actually is, theirs being expressed as climate, even and predictable and not worth noticing. They found it necessary to discourage this American with the French name, this Lieutenant Maury, from trying to get land meteorology included in the agenda. When he agreed to limit the discussion to the sea everyone was much relieved. The meeting was his idea in the first place, and for a while it had begun to look as if it might get a bit sticky. Brussels was the scene of the little conclave, and representatives from ten nations met to agree on a uniform reporting form for abstract logs, so that it would be easier to use the information for chart and record making.

Mat made the whole affair as important as he could. He had, however, brought his daughters Betty and Nannie and his wards Ellen Herndon and Sallie Fontaine along with him, and they were rather a nuisance, making no bones about the trip being theirs, suffering nobly through meeting famous scientists and giggling for hours afterward, and bearing up as best they could under the presence of the "old gentleman." [5] But Mat smiled at them, happy with his increasing fame, now augmented by the first international meteorological convention (nautical).

Criticisms of his country's policies both at home and abroad were expressed to him pointedly while he was in England. He was taunted with an *Uncle Tom's Cabin* view of slavery, and the Mexican War and the ridiculous tenets of the Compromise of 1850, which included the Fugitive Slave Act. "Are slaves really hunted by bloodhounds?" "Could I get a job as engineer on the Underground Railroad?" "Do you know Harriet Beecher Stowe?" He had to admit that, owning no slaves himself, still he was committed to the section of the country that supported slavery. In vain, he tried to explain slavery: that the Negroes were inferior, incapable of taking care of themselves, that the southern planter did them a favor by looking after them; that they were childish and stupid so it took great patience to handle them. That there were fine Negroes he knew for a fact, and their masters loved them and were loved in return. He quoted a saw long in favor in the South: "Yankees love Negroes as a race and hate them as individuals; southerners hate Negroes as a race and love them as individuals." He quoted his relatives who had described a slave of theirs as "a member of our servant family." That was the ideal of the South—a big, happy farm family. The southerner was a superior breed of person; no viciousness would ever be inflicted on the helpless black man; besides, there were laws that prohibited slaveowners from killing their slaves. The British somehow thought southerners were just like the other folks in the world, and kept on being anti-slavery. They had reason to feel superior: they had just passed a law prohibiting the employment of boys under ten in coal mines.

Back home, while the British were demonstrating their sophistication by fighting an unnecessary war in the Crimea, Maury was again busy at his Observatory. In addition to the meteorological records, there were terrestrial-magnetism observations to make; the usual repair, purchasing, and issue of instruments, charts, and books; the star catalog to work on; the chronometers to be star-checked. Work on the charts continued, and when his nephew Dabney, stationed in Philadelphia that winter, went to see Mr. Biddle about a business matter for his uncle, the publisher suggested that part of the *Sailing Directions* be printed in a book for the general public.

Maury called it *The Physical Geography of the Sea.*

Useful as the *Sailing Directions* were, they were liable to be regarded as technical matters of interest only to sailors. *The Physical Geography of the Sea* made a bid for regard as a work of science. Putting some speeches together with extracts from the *Sailing Directions*, Maury hastily got out the first book on oceanography. Others, notably Major James Rennell, who in 1832 had published a book and charts on the Gulf Stream, Alexander Dallas Bache, Alexander von Humboldt, Alexander Dalrymple, Marin Jansen, and Keith Johnston, had also done notable work on various areas or phases of the ocean complex.

The original edition of *The Physical Geography of the Sea* was full of errors, an inevitable result of the hasty way in which it was gotten together. That he went off half-cocked may be inferred from Mat's introduction to the sixth edition: *As may be supposed, facts are sometimes misinterpreted or not understood when first developed. Whenever subsequent research shows such to have been the case I have not hesitated to tear down whatever of conjecture or theory may have been built on unstable foundations, and to reconstruct according to the best lights.*

The first edition is the reason so many writers on the ocean today accuse him of not attributing the path of the Gulf Stream to the Coriolis Effect. But in the sixth edition (1856) he says on page 42: *The effect of diurnal rotation upon the winds and upon the currents of the sea is admitted by all—the trade-winds derive their* easting *from it.* He then goes on to describe the path of the Gulf Stream as following that of a cannon ball shot from Bemini to England, which it does. To see for yourself the effect of rotation upon a natural effort to follow a straight line, put a record on the record player, start it up, and attempt to draw a straight line across it with a brush full of paint. The record turns, the straight line curves grandly, just as the Gulf Stream sweeps across the ocean.

His first edition also held errors or misconceptions about such subjects as the open sea in the Arctic, the Atlantic basin, and the concentration of salt in sea water, all of which he recast into more plausible form in later editions.

So casual an attitude toward sacred scientific truth shocked those savants referred to by Maury as "closet" scientists. But scientists such as the secretary of the Smithsonian Institution were men whose characters as scientists were the clearest of crystal: no such mistakes ever bore their names; they would have preferred to have died unknown rather than have published something ridiculously incorrect. No such scruples deterred Mat Maury from being the first oceanographer; errors could always be corrected in a subsequent edition, so why worry about it?

On one matter he refused to be corrected. Sir Charles Lyell had published his *Principles of Geology* in 1830 and Mat knew the book, had quoted from it. But Lyell, to whose shirt tail Darwin clung for reassurance in his theories of natural selection, had upset the biblical history of the creation of the world. He destroyed the theory of cataclysmic changes bringing about the present earth structure, and published the first tables showing the long epochs of rock formation going back millions of years. Maury refused to accept any theory of creation other than the Bible version. Consequently the gradual accumulation of new discoveries, when added to Maury's habit of bringing the Bible in to explain disputed matters, gives the book today an odd, archaic cast. For instance, on the subject of whether sea water was ever not salt: *On the second day of creation the waters were gathered together unto one place, and the dry land appeared. Before that period, therefore, there were no rivers, and consequently no washings of brine by mists, nor dew, nor rains from the valleys among the hills. The water covered the earth. This is the account of Revelation, and when we come to examine the fossil remains that are buried in the mountains and scattered over the plains, we have as much reason to say that the sea was salt when it covered or nearly covered the earth, as the naturalist, when he sees a skull or bone whitening on the wayside, has to say that it was once covered with flesh.* According to the scriptural account, though, no living things inhabited the seas until the fifth day, or after the waters had receded—so how did those fossil shells get in the mountains?

He also used the book to advertise his Wind and Current Charts and put in long accounts of sailing voyages around the Cape, showing how the winners always followed his charts. Evidence that a great part of the book had been written on government time and published to Maury's profit also dismayed a certain class of people.

However, this first attempt at oceanography was far from being all wrong, nor deserving of contempt. His map of the Gulf Stream is still excellent by today's standards. He made the first orographic map showing the contours of the bottom of the North Atlantic, the first map ever made of the ocean

108

floor. The book has passages that show that if Maury had had that infinite capacity for taking pains that characterizes genius, he would have produced a great work. But he dictated the book hastily, often to his children, and failed to pursue his facts without regard to preconceived notions. He had the chance to write one of the world's great books, and muffed it.

Honors and awards continued to come to him, mostly from foreign governments and from struggling young American scientific organizations looking for wealthy sponsors. He could truthfully feel, and often said, that the world was a better place because he had lived. He had done more than any man then living to make the sea safe for mankind.

Could he go along peacefully, calm and assured in his later days that all was well with his world? His eldest daughter married a young Washington attorney, a distant Maury relation, and Nannie married a wealthy Virginian planter named Corbin. Matthew Fontaine Maury, Junior, called Matsy by the family and Scip or Brave by his father; and Lucy Minor, whom her Pa called Sat Sing, were the last of his eight children. Evenings they would gather around the center table under the whaleoil lamp to study or sew, and Mat would dictate to one of his daughters while taking a walk around the room and smoking for relaxation. How spoiled his children were at this time is all too evident in the petulant notes they add to the letters, complaining about having to write them. But they were happy together. The usual visiting around went on continually and Mrs. Maury spent a good deal of her time in Fredericksburg. Richard was a law student at the University, misbehaving and falling down in his grades. Davy Jones, a pleasant lad with a pronounced lisp, was preparing for the Virginia Military Institute. Dabney was in New Mexico with his regiment.

Giving him one more thing to worry about, the Kansas-

Nebraska Act was passed by a Congress seemingly blind to the fact that Kansas was right next to slaveholding Missouri. "Popular sovereignty" meant that pro-slavery men and abolitionists both poured in and each tried to scare the other group away. No blood was shed for several months, however. Then it was obvious that each side in the angry dissension was ready to fight.

If this trouble in Kansas was a chill hint of disaster to come, Maury was now to run into real trouble. His long list of naval reforms had included weeding out the deadwood in the officer ranks so that promising younger men could be promoted. A Naval Retiring Board was set up under congressional authorization and 71 officers were, as a result, placed on a "reserved on leave of absence pay" list.

Matthew Fontaine Maury was one of them.

On September 17, 1855, Secretary of the Navy James C. Dobbin sent Mat official notice that he was now on the reserve list, with full leave-of-absence pay—and that *he was to continue his regular duties as head of the National Observatory.*

Maury was so affronted that his behavior became almost demented. He could not think, talk, or write on any other subject for months: he'd been unjustly attacked, kept on his job at less than half pay, when he had done the Navy nothing but good! Challenged, the Secretary of the Navy passed the buck to President Pierce, who passed it back again. The press took up the cry and demanded Maury's reinstatement. Congress had to investigate, whereupon Jefferson Davis, Judah P. Benjamin, and Stephen Mallory proved noticeably cool toward the friend of the Yankee traders. Mat remembered now that two of the members of the Retiring Board had been reported by him to the Secretary of the Navy for ignoring the ruling requiring them to complete abstract logs for the use of Lieutenant Maury for each voyage. In

110

fact, he could just about go down the list of members of that board and know what they had against him. But the Maury honor had been injured. He would never give up. He stopped star-gazing, and all his other work was let go.[6] He devoted his entire time to clearing his name. Since someone had said his crippled condition was responsible, he took to walking from the Navy Department (then next door to the White House) out to the Observatory, scorning even the aid of his cane. His distressed family could hardly bear the sight of him limping up the drive, pale, exhausted, stubborn.[7]

Unrelenting in his determination to win reinstatement, he cast about for ways to keep his name before the public. The most vigorously pursued of these was a plan to form a central weather bureau, receiving reports of storms by telegraph.

NOTES TO CHAPTER SIX

1. *Man Makes Himself*, by Childe, page 104.

2. On an errata sheet in *Astronomical and Meteorological Observations Made During the Year 1871 at the United States Naval Observatory*, by Sands. The address is given as 2222-24 Pennsylvania Avenue in the text of this book.

3. He invented the screw propeller about like Morse invented the telegraph, out of bits and pieces of other's work earlier.

4. The meeting was picayune: the matters decided on, for international cooperation in recording the weather at sea, are still in operation.

5. Maury's children prior to the war were full of high spirits and disrespect for their elders and other symptoms of good fortune and financial ease.

6. When Gilliss took over the Observatory in 1861 he found the observers had gone on with their work, but no reduc-

CHAPTER SEVEN

Henry and the Smithsonian

AN IMMENSE AMOUNT of to-do had been going on about the will of that James Smithson ever since his death in 1829. It was 1838 before the United States government got the money, and then another eight years were spent trying to figure out how to use the bequest in the manner meant by Smithson. It was expressed ambiguously—that "for the increase and diffusion of knowledge among men"—and everyone with a pet project, from agricultural colleges to weather bureaus, tried to get the money appropriated to use for it. But all the projects had the object of bettering one field of knowledge, and that seemed hardly what Smithson had had in mind. In an earlier will he had left the money to the Royal Society; later, disenchanted with its personnel and policies, he had written the provisions in force at the time of his death.

While still at Princeton Joseph Henry had made a suggested program for the Smithsonian to follow, in which the income from the invested principal was to be used to pay for original-research projects, courses of lectures, and the printing and distribution of scientific papers. The secretary of the Smithsonian would thus occupy a modest office space of two rooms or so, and supervise the financial disbursement of the Institution's income.

Congress received his plan with thanks and immediately set out to improve on it. There should be an imposing building, something the public could appreciate. There should be a museum to house the objects brought back by the Wilkes Exploring Expedition. There should also be a library, and an art gallery. They would make the showplace of Washington out of the Englishman's funds. There were few enough notable sights in the city of magnificent distances (i.e., nothing), as Washington had been labeled.

On December 23, 1846, the site for the building was decided on: fifty-two acres on "a tract of public land denominated '*the Mall*,' the grounds [to] extend from Seventh to Twelfth streets, east and west, and from the canal to D Street north and south." [1] The Henrys had barely returned to Washington after spending Christmas at Princeton with brother Stephen Alexander and his family when the Board of Regents announced that a plan by James Renwick had been adopted for the Smithsonian building.

James Renwick's Cathedral of St. Patrick and his Grace Church in New York suit their purpose well enough, but other samples of his ornate style throughout New York State were, as Henry knew, "curiouser and curiouser." Nothing was ever to mellow his attitude toward the Smithsonian's building: he referred to it as a Norman cenotaph in memory of half the Smithsonian funds. Each stone was quarried out of his back, it seemed, but while it grew slowly it grew steadily. The cornerstone was laid according to Masonic ritual on May 1, 1847, before a crowd of 6,000. It was completed in 1855, although parts of it had been in use long

114

before then, and the work of the Institution had been assiduously carried out by its secretary and his staff from 1846 on.

The red sandstone building itself is so unusual in the gallery of cold white Grecian temples that are the predominant Washington style that it makes an unforgettable impression on all who see it. Unfortunately it has long been the butt of sophomoric architectural critics: "Weird monstrosity," "strange mish-mash," "Victorian hodgepodge," "that Gothic horror," "red nightmare," and so on. I like the Smithsonian building. In my lonely, dreamy, book-ridden childhood the tallest of the nine towers, the near-twin towers on either side of the rose window in the front, were "the topless towers of Ilium." Almost all the other towers have high-peaked roofs. Not these. I remember it one spring Saturday, in a fine morning mist, its fretted stones and spires glowing garnet-red across the wide Mall where the new grass shone brilliantly green, as much a fairy castle as any of Never-Never Land. And full of treasures. Actually, the building is an example of twelfth-century architecture—we call it Romanesque today—with the tall, rounded arches that immediately pre-date Gothic. We speak of it in a kinder mood than before: the Abbaye-aux-Hommes was its chief inspiration and the apse of that great cathedral is charmingly reproduced as a chapel in miniature in the west wing. If the "old building" at the Smithsonian can hold out another hundred years, people may get over their usual dislike for the too-near past. Washington would look awfully cold without it.

As if to make sure Joseph Henry would never like the building, the first publication authorized by the Board of Regents was not on a scientific subject. Robert Dale Owen's *Hints on Public Architecture* was an encomium on Renwick's plan.

This Board of Regents had been set up by Congress to act as a buffer between it and a salaried director. It was composed of a chancellor, at this time the Vice President of the United States, six members of Congress, and six others, who were supposed to be scientists. Alexander Dallas Bache was one of the latter. Soon to be appointed from Congress was Jefferson Davis. One of the first official acts requested of Henry by the Board of Regents was to appoint an assistant, and he named Professor Jewett, who was librarian. Henry was outspokenly opposed to having the Smithsonian support a library, which would duplicate the work of the Library of Congress, but Professor Jewett and Rufus Choate, the bibliophile congressman [2] who was a member of the Board of Regents, were close friends. Anyway, Jewett was the only other employee of the Institution at this time, so Henry had to name him. Half of the yearly income of the Smithsonian was to go to buy books for this—to Henry—unnecessary library. The Regents next ordered that he spend $10,000 of the Institution's funds to plant trees on the Mall around the building. He complied, but from then on, where matters contrary to his plan were concerned, he seems to have dragged his feet.

Joseph Henry felt that he had given up much to accept the responsibility of administering the Smithsonian. And reponsibility was the way he regarded this trust. There had been many promising avenues of investigation opening up before him in his work at Princeton, all of which he had renounced upon going to Washington. His friend Bache, who had all but forced Henry upon the Regents and vice versa, had had a face-saver included in the list of qualifications for the position of secretary. It said that this person should be a scientist capable of carrying on scientific investigation to redound to the credit of the Smithsonian. However, Joseph, with that great pride in his integrity and realizing that most people would not know about that qualification, refused to enter into any field of experiment not related to problems faced by the government or to fields of endeavor that should be administered by the government, and then only those not being investigated by other reputable scientists. No one could say he was using the Englishman's money to make himself famous.

Mr. Smithson's half-million dollars was loaned by law to the United States Treasury at a permanent 6-per-cent interest and the Scot in Joseph Henry stood guard over it like a Border collie over his herd. To the Regents' embarrassment and amusement the schoolteacher in their secretary took over at his annual accountings of the Institution's funds. He would set up a blackboard and, nervous and perspiring, write out and explain to them the year's financial activities.[3] It was very gratifying, though, to see the Institution's income fussed over and explained to the final cent by a man so famous and so transparently honest. Perhaps he was a great man because nothing was too small for his attention. He felt that it was petty to be important.

Henry's most serious problem in getting the Institution started on its way was that there was no precedent upon which to act, no matter what came up. A nervous twitch of his upper lip would appear when the decisions were difficult to make. However, once he had made up his mind his conscience was assured that the question had been investigated from every angle and his decision had enough merit for him to defend it.

At first the Regents had an unnecessary amount to say about managing the Institution they had been so eager to hand over to Joseph, but soon the novelty wore off and he was left to do the work. By the end of February 1847 the lecture series was started with William Scoresby speaking in Odd Fellows Hall on "The Construction and Use of the

117

Rosse Telescope." The first publication instigated by Henry was the one generally known as the initial offering of the Smithsonian, *Ancient Monuments of the Mississippi Valley*, by Squir and Davis, which included parts of a paper by Locke on the ancient mounds in Ohio. At this time the Capitol was being rebuilt in part, and Henry was called upon to determine which type of stone would be the strongest to use in its construction. The only scientific paper he published during this first year with the Smithsonian was one on magnetism for the *Encyclopedia Americana*. The buying of books proceeded *very* slowly.

The Henrys' life in Washington was much tied in with local and visiting intellectuals. During the winter season, when Congress was in session, Washington was a lively town, a-swirl with partly hostile, partly overlapping cliques—the various political groups; the diplomatic set; the old Georgetown society; nearby Maryland and Virginia society; that set of lavish entertainers, the lobbyists; armed-forces families; and the upper echelon of government employees. Professor Henry was friends, either by duty or choice, with many people in many of these groups. Sometimes pressures were put upon him that he resented, and sometimes he would complain that it was difficult to be an honest man in Washington, but he was tactful enough to get out of many situations and sensible enough to know when he had to put up with something he didn't like. Professor Bache and his wife had frequent informal gatherings at their house, next to the row of Coast Survey buildings, where those geraniums still curtained the parlor windows. One Christmas Eve Bache dressed up as Santa Claus in a moth-eaten fur coat and handed out the presents with a choice morsel of doggerel poetry to accompany each one, and dark, handsome, dignified Jefferson Davis sang an Indian song he had learned when on the frontier with the Army. Thirty years later his

118

wife, Varina, was to look back on that night, the yellow candle flames like stars clustered around the room; the wood fire blazing cheerily away beneath the white mantel covered with holly; the velvet smell of that special bayberry candle that Emily Bache had ordered from her home in Rhode Island; the long table spread with delicious food in the big dining room where surveying instruments hung for ornaments on the walls; and the happy faces and the cheerful talk and all the good hopes for the morrow. And against the windows the rattle of sleet.

Morse's telegraph was so successful that he was constantly suing and being sued for infringement of patent rights. Invariably Joseph Henry was subpoenaed, the claim being made that the electromagnet and relay and series of batteries without which the Morse telegraph was useless were in the public domain owing to Henry's failure to patent. Because Henry could not say under oath that Morse had invented the telegraph, Morse got mightily peeved with him—even though there is every indication that it was Henry's influence with the Commissioner of Patents that got Morse's original patent extended despite all the litigation. Certainly Henry seems to have done everything he could to help Morse, short of perjuring himself by saying that Morse had invented the things that everyone, including Morse's partners, knew that Henry had invented himself.

Henry was very fond of the telegraph. He liked to sit in a telegraph-company office and watch the busy operators and the coming and going of words along that immensely satisfying wire. In one of his scientific papers [4] he tells of such an occurrence at the office in Philadelphia:

The operator at each end of the line announced at the same time a storm at Washington and another at Jersey City. The portion of the circuit which entered the building

119

happened to pass within less than an inch of the wire which served to form the connection with the earth. Across this space, every few minutes, a series of sparks in rapid succession was observed to pass; and when one of the storms arrived so near Philadelphia that the lightning could be seen, each series of sparks was found to be simultaneous with a flash in the heavens.

Seeing scenes such as that no doubt led Henry to write in his notebook in February of 1849 [5]: *I have had in my mind a fine scheme with the telegraph. Instantaneous observations on the Aurora, on the thunderstorm, the beginnings of storms, etc.* He added on March 12, 1849: *Mr. Redfield highly approves plan of using telegraph for meteorological purposes. The following should be made stations: Portland, Boston, New York, Philadelphia, Baltimore, Washington, Norfolk, Charleston, Savannah, Mobile, Pensacola, Augusta, Nashville, New Orleans (northern and southern), Galena, St. Louis, Chicago, Buffalo, Albany (western). Times—morning, noon and night, or morning and night. Most important observations: 1. Barometer 2. Face of the sky 3. Direction and force of the wind.* And on May 19: *Wrote to Judge McLean to give me an account of his obs. on thunderstorms. Thunderstorms come from the west at Washington—on the opposite side of the river divide, one part down, the other to Baltimore. Prepare circular relative to storms of this kind.*

Scattered people here and there around the world had been interested in the weather on land, but it remained for the Americans to encourage the doing of something about it. William Redfield and James Espey, following Franklin's original investigations, got into a public controversy on the paths followed by storms. Elias Loomis, reading these argumentative articles, began to have ideas of his own and came up with lines called isobars which connect all areas with the same barometric pressure on a map, and lines called isotherms to show temperatures the same way. Professor Espey, whose researches had led him to be called "the Storm King," fell upon this idea of Loomis's and carried it off to Congress, demanding that the government set up stations to observe the weather. This was in 1842, and John Quincy Adams, then serving in Congress, sneered at the "necromancer" in his diary. Earlier, in 1817, Commissioner of the General Land Office Josiah Meigs had started meteorological observations daily in scattered land offices throughout the country; and two years after that the Army commenced to keep weather records upon the insistence of the Surgeon General. Now, with the innovations of Loomis, and some from France, Espey felt that the observation of the weather approached a science, and with the increasing use of the telegraph, it began to look as if foretelling the weather, or at least the approach of storms, would be the next logical step. Joseph Henry had been interested in meteorology since his early days at Albany Academy and the subject of thunderstorms particularly fascinated him. Espey and Loomis joined with Henry and the forces of the Smithsonian to get a group of volunteers enlisted all over the country to send daily weather reports to the Smithsonian in 1849. More than six hundred volunteered and about two hundred fifty sent in conscientious reports using forms devised by Arnold Guyot, another pioneer in weather matters and a close friend of Henry. Within a few years a large map with movable figures placed in the entryway of the Smithsonian showed the weather picture of the whole country. Beneath the weather map became one of the town's fashionable meeting places.

On April 10, 1849, the east wing of the Smithsonian building was completed. It contained the lecture room, labora-

tories, and apparatus rooms. Soon, in order to be closer to
the building, Henry moved with his wife and daughters to
another rooming house, this time at Thirteenth Street and
Pennsylvania Avenue.

A defect in the Smithsonian building started Joseph
Henry on a field of research that was to interest him the rest
of his life. The lecture room was quite attractive, with oak-
paneled walls, round-topped windows filled with trefoils, and
pleasant proportions. There was only one thing wrong with
it: you couldn't hear in it. Every sound made on the speak-
er's platform was swallowed up as if by magic. Henry began
a long series of investigations in acoustics that was eventually to lead him to the foghorns of the Lighthouse Service.
The lecture room was rearranged by trial and error and
notes taken on what processes gave the best results, it was
enlarged to seat a thousand people, and the acoustics improved a great deal.

Eighteen fifty was a banner year for the Smithsonian.
The library had just been moved over from the Patent Office,
along with Professor Jewett and his demands for books, more
books. The reports on the progress of science, started the
previous year, were well received and enthusiastically pushed
forward. An appropriation was made by Congress for a
natural-history collection, most distressing to Henry, since
the last thing he wanted was for the Smithsonian to become
a museum. But the Smithsonian seemed as determined as
water to find its own level and developed into itself despite
Congress, the Regents, Secretary Henry, Professor Jewett,
and the demands of the public. Henry got a well-known
ornithologist, Spencer Fullerton Baird, to take the museum
in charge. To Baird, an old shoe box full of seashells anony-
mously deposited at the front door was a potential treasure
trove. As fond of things in themselves as Henry was of ideas,
he kept the museum together and growing until it should

come into its own. Henry would look after his bustling assistant with the flying whiskers, and that nervous twitch would appear in his upper lip.

At least some of the Smithsonian's funds were used as Henry wished. The series of explorations in lesser-known parts of the country, the most important of which were Major Powell's in the Southwest, and those in Central and South America, and to the polar regions were started this year. The Smithsonian's section of the Mall had been enclosed with an iron fence and profusely planted with trees, but the general appearance was chaotic in the extreme. President Fillmore gave Henry permission to have the New York landscape architect, Andrew Downing, plan walks and drives and flowerbeds on the grounds, and soon the place was a most attractive park. Downing was drowned following a Hudson River steamboat explosion shortly thereafter and a monument to his memory was raised on the grounds by popular subscription. The urn with his name on it is still there, but his design of the park was erased with the formation of the open Mall that stretches now without so much as a bush to grace it from the Capitol to Fourteenth Street, where they let some trees grow around Washington Monument.

The trouble Henry had been having with the library finally boiled into the open. He discharged Jewett, the librarian, and also Mr. Blodgett, who had been hired to help with the meteorological work and who had been taking sides with Jewett. The result of this was a congressional investigation of the handling of the Smithsonian funds. One of the committee members turned in a pro-library report, two turned in pro-Henry reports, and two abstained. The whole matter was turned back to the Regents with a memo noting that there was a duplication of effort with the activities of the Library of Congress in the library scheme. The Regents sustained Henry in firing Jewett and Blodgett and admitted that the plan for the Smithsonian approved by Congress set no minimum amount that had to be spent yearly on books. After that Henry was free to run the Smithsonian and spend its money without having the amount allocated to each field of activity dictated to him. He still had the museum and the art gallery around his neck, and in every yearly report to the Regents begged to be relieved of them. He thought they were needed, but by being too limited in the number of people who could see them, they fell outside the scope of the Englishman's will and should be financed by the government. He made no excuses for the lecture series, however, although they benefited only a limited number of localites.

During the winter season, the Washington *Daily Star* reported the activities at the Smithsonian frequently. One of Henry's pet projects was the exchange system, under which, for example, the skull of a North American mammal would be traded for one from the Old World, or an Indian blanket for a ceremonial device from Australia. These acquisitions were reported in the papers, as were the discoveries of comets and scientific matters which were gotten from the trading about of information with other countries. The lecture series was highly successful, the *Star* urging newcomers to be sure to attend as they were always of excellent quality. One series by Professor Mitchell, on astronomy, was, to the dismay of the savants and the delight of the audience, attended by Mrs. Amelia Bloomer in her namesakes. Mitchell had a crowded hall to speak to for the entire series.

The *Star* noted other interesting items that season: the impounding of nineteen hogs to serve as a warning that it was against the law for hogs to run loose south of Massachusetts Avenue; a woman being sent to jail for beating her eight-year-old Negro slave ("we have laws in the South to provide punishment for such a thing," the *Star* commented indignantly) ; fresh beef was ten cents a pound and chickens two

124

for fifty cents at Central Market, which was at the foot of Seventh Street on the canal, between Pennsylvania Avenue and that odorous ditch; a concert was held at Carusi's saloon; the hop at Willard's was a smashing success; shawls were all the fashion; action by the Navy Retiring Board placing Captain Joseph Smith of the Bureau of Yards and Docks on half pay was condemned; the governor of Kansas asked for troops to keep order in that strife-ridden territory.

The editor greeted joyfully news of the Hughes telegraph. The Morse company did nothing but "screw and grind, grind and screw" their charges to the newspapers. Hughes was implored to deliver them from this odious Morse monopoly. Playfully, he commented: "Lieutenant Maury has demonstrated that, by wind and wave, it is downstream from our country to all the world; and that all nations must ascend to reach us." Mr. Ericsson, the marine inventor (not yet, but soon, of the *Monitor*), lost part of two fingers in the explosion of his new caloric engine. Dr. Linton, who was surgeon on board the United States brig *Somers* when the Spencer mutiny took place, was lynched in Laredo, Texas, after shooting two men.[6] The Know-Nothing riots were condemned heartily, and heavily-padded lists of casualties were printed for a week.

In the summer cholera epidemics were common. The largest and most prosperous towns seemed to have the worst ones. Panics and railroad accidents ran the epidemics a lethal second. The Washington papers published lengthy articles on the cholera situation, telling everyone where not to go, while admitting to only one case in town. Much "summer sickness" was acknowledged, however. Summers in Washington were fairly miserable, with flies, mosquitoes, thickly humid heat, violent thunderstorms, and crowds of toughs who delighted in throwing firecrackers under spirited carriage horses and beating up stray passers-by. It was no safer to walk down the street in Washington in 1855 than it is today.

Mrs. Henry and the children went visiting in the summer, to Philadelphia or to Princeton or to Long Branch, or even to Albany. Joseph would pay a visit to Dallas Bache at one of his survey stations, and then start on the pleasing problems of the Lighthouse Service, to the Board of which he had been appointed when it was founded in 1852. On Staten Island was a sort of lighthouse depot, where equipment was repaired and even invented, and here Henry set up a light-measuring apparatus to see what fuel was best, and cheapest, for the huge Argand burners of the lighthouses. One of the first accomplishments of the Lighthouse Board had been the introduction of Fresnel lenses. These look like circular venetian blinds and concentrate the beam of light to its most usable form. They were being imported from France at great expense, and now the problem was to save money on fuel to make up for the outlay on lenses. Whale oil and rape-seed oil were the fuels in most common use, but whale oil was getting steadily more expensive and rape seed was little grown in this country. Lard oil had been tried in small lamps with little success, but because of its low price Henry kept on tinkering with it (in the face of great opposition from the whaling industry; he could well complain of the pressures that were put on him), until one day it occurred to him to try it in one of the big Argand burners under actual conditions of use. It sizzled and fumed for a moment, then burst into a grand circle of flame. Being addicted to unsedate behavior in a moment of triumph, the big man leaped in the air with joy.[7] The recalcitrant lard oil had only needed to be subjected to great heat, a lot of it burning at once, to be perfectly usable in the lighthouse service, at a saving of a million dollars or so to the government.

The Lighthouse Service cutters *Mistletoe*, *Cactus*, and *Putnam* were one or the other or all at his disposal for acoustic experiments. He spent as much time at sea as many a naval officer, testing fog-signaling equipment, and temporarily escaping from eccentric inventors of alleged fog-signaling equipment. Henry was the most accessible of men, over-accessible in fact, so these crackpots were always able to get his ear and waste his time sooner or later. Perhaps he didn't really need an excuse for going out on the little *Mistletoe;* he seemed to be very fond of the ship.

All this time, back in New York, Samuel F. B. Morse was walking the floor and stewing in a juice of moral indignation. He was a great one for getting upset by remembering what he considered injustices, recalling over and over occurrences that he didn't like. Joseph Henry said that by a lucky stroke of fortune he was able to remember the good things in his past over the bad. Poor Morse was just the opposite. He would work himself into bilious attacks by putting all his concentration on unpleasant memories. Many years before, in Rome, he had neglected one day to remove his Protestant hat when a Roman Catholic religious procession passed and an outraged officer of the Papal States army had knocked him down. Morse brooded about that indignity; himself, a free American, beaten into a filthy gutter by a servant of the Pope. He and some others founded an anti-Catholic political party, the Know-Nothings, or Native Americans, and he was disastrously defeated when he ran for mayor of New York on the Nativist ticket.

When not brooding over this he would brood over the sufferings he had undergone while inventing and trying to interest an indifferent world in his telegraph. He had gone hungry many a time, his children had grown up without him, his wife had died young, there was no sacrifice he had not made to make rapid communication available (for a royalty that made him a millionaire) to the world.

Now it seemed to him that Joseph Henry, that idealistic fool, was trying to rob him of his glory. People *would* refer to Henry as the inventor of the telegraph when *he*, Samuel

Finley Breese Morse, was the inventor. He had written a history of how he had invented it, with only a bare mention of Henry's name, to prove his claims. That his associates disagreed only made him surer of his opinion. At last he stopped ignoring Henry and published a direct attack on him. This amazing work must have been composed during one of Morse's bilious spells; nothing but pure churlishness would explain anything so ill-humored and biased. The 96-page pamphlet enlarged on the following: *1st. I certainly shall show that I have manifested every disposition to give due credit to Professor Henry, but under the hasty impression that he deserved credit for discoveries in science bearing upon the telegraph, I did actually give him a degree of credit not only beyond what he had received at that time from the scientific world, but a degree of credit to which subsequent research has proved him not to be entitled. 2d. I shall show that I am not indebted to him for any discovery in science bearing on the telegraph, and that all discoveries of principles having this bearing were made not by Professor Henry, but by others and prior to any experiments of Professor Henry in the science of electro-magnetism. 3d. I shall further show that the claim set up for Professor Henry to the invention of an important part of my telegraph system, has no validity in fact.*[8]

Professor Gale, Morse's associate who had been teaching natural philosophy at New York University while Morse was teaching painting there and trying to get his telegraph to work, at once wrote Henry that when he had first seen Morse's telegraph he had been using Sturgeon's feeble electromagnet and that he, Gale, had told him about Henry's electromagnet.[9] He assured Henry that any time he wanted to reply to Morse's lies that he would back him up.

Henry characteristically couldn't make up his mind what to do. At last he decided the dignified thing would be to

128

ignore Morse and his nonsense. That wasn't satisfactory, for all of the Regents and Congress were not aware of the actual history of the telegraph. No matter how he assured himself, and was reassured by his friends, he knew that there was a stain on his reputation. How often he had regretted leaving Princeton! But he had allowed himself to be tempted by the picture of Joseph Henry directing a great scientific institution, regarded as a benefactor of mankind, and for what! For what! To be defamed and insulted in a telegrapher's pamphlet!

While all this was going on the Smithsonian building was completed. The Henrys moved into a large, sunny apartment that had been set up for them on the second floor of the east wing; the library (which they still had with them) was moved into the west wing or "chapel," Professor Baird's museum was set up downstairs in the main part of the building, a pair of gracious, curving stairs reached up from the marble-floored lobby to the lecture room upstairs, the exchange section was set up beneath the Henrys' apartment, and the 90-odd rooms in the building, including those in the towers, were quickly put to use. William J. Rhees, his clerical assistant, and family moved into a small apartment, and Mr. De Bust, who could make anything with his hands, lived there close by his workshop, and old Mr. McRake, the janitor, and his wife lived there. Likewise, penniless scientists engaged in research, and visitors such as Professor Espey who came on prolonged stays. And Hannah and Margaret Patterson, their Irish cook and housemaid, and little Thomas Datcher, who had no home and came from nobody knew where, and who ran errands and carried the coal and made himself useful.[10]

From the west-facing chapel tower one could see the copper dome of the Naval Observatory on its low hill beside the Potomac.

On January 10, 1856, the United States Agricultural

CHAPTER EIGHT

"*Just Before the Battle, Mother*"

THE WASHINGTON *Daily Star* reported the proceedings of the United States Agricultural Society at length, because the group was primarily interested in establishing agricultural colleges throughout the country, as land-grant colleges, partly to be used by the government for experimental farms. The South was opposed to any such idea, claiming that it gave the federal government control over state business.[1]

Dr. Beechman, of New York, presented the following resolution: Resolved, *That agriculture and other great interests of the State would, in the opinion of this society, be materially benefitted by extending to the land the system of meteorological cooperation and research which has done so much and is doing so much for commerce and navigation at sea; and that this Society does hereby earnestly recommend*

131

such extension to the favorable consideration of Congress. This resolution is being debated as we go to press. Lieut. Maury, Prof. Henry and other eminent gentlemen are participating.[2]

"Participating," the *Star* said; actually, they were shouting insults at each other. The next day it continued the story:

C. B. Calvert, Esq., of Maryland, replied to Professor Henry's remarks, especially his insinuation that Lieut. Maury was not entitled to the credit of having made meteorological observation practically useful. With due respect to Professor Henry and the Smithsonian, he would not have the matter pass from the hands of that eminent and distinguished man, who had not only proved himself a scientific man, but a man of practical science.

Judge S. H. Huntington, of Connecticut, hoped that a committee would be appointed to consider the subject, before presenting it to Congress.

C. B. Calvert, Esq., objected to this, as calculated to detract from the honor belonging to Lieut. Maury.

Lieut. Maury, Judge Huntington, Professor Henry and Horace Greeley spoke on the question of reference to a committee.

Major Poore, regretting that the discussion was becoming a personal scientific quarrel, into which such subjects had been introduced as illegitimate, as was "the scion of the House of Northumberland," who had been alluded to, moved the previous question. The motion was sustained and the resolution was then carried.

That night there was wrath in the Smithsonian. Not only had the delicate subject of Mr. Smithson's illegitimacy been flung in Henry's face, but practical science had been preferred to pure science, while that Maury fellow was memorialized to Congress as if he had invented meteorology. And in a building built with the illegitimate's funds and in which a weather map was then on display! Fortunately his friends came and explained what was behind the resolution. It had been intended only as a means of praising Maury without actually naming him, as a reward for his work in oceanography and to improve his chances of getting back into active service despite the Retiring Board.

Mollified, Henry calmed down. But whereas he had held small regard for Maury before, now he felt an active animosity toward him. He would out-meteorology him, or know why not.

At the Observatory things were the most cheerful since the Retiring Board had lowered the boom. If he could get Congress to back him as head of land meteorology, Maury would be assured of regaining his rightful place in the Navy, and probably a captaincy and five years' back pay in that rank, besides.

The Agricultural Bureau of the Patent Office and the friends of the Smithsonian saw to it that Senator Harlan's bill before Congress to vote Maury head of land meteorology was defeated.

This was the year the shooting started in Kansas, the year Buchanan was elected president. It was the last time the South would be able to run the government. Their political party was collapsing into one so purely sectional they would never again get enough sympathizers from the North to make their way of life assured. They began to turn to themselves, believing themselves self-sufficient (they had to bring engineers down from the North to run their trains). "Disunion" was talked everywhere below Mason and Dixon's line. And

the two most famous intellects in the country were squabbling
in public and private over who would get credit for thinking
up the use of the telegraph for sending weather news.

Maury, still on half pay, was still determined to do half-
pay work. He spent a great deal of time attending to his in-
vestments, corresponded at length with Cyrus Field about
the proposed Atlantic cable that was to be laid on the plateau
which Lieutenant Berryman's soundings on the steamer *Arctic*
had brought to light, and went on a very successful New England lecture tour. In between times he tried to politic himself
in as head of a central weather-reporting station.

It must have been very difficult for people such as Senator
John Bell of Tennessee, who made a pro-Maury speech de-
nouncing the Navy Retiring Board before Congress and
spent Christmas with the Henrys at the Smithsonian, to see
this childish display of temperament. But by and large the
important people from the South seem to have taken Henry's
side against Maury and the Navy. In fact, Henry's reputa-
tion-by-association with the southern cause was strengthened
in the public's eye when he refused Horace Greeley of the
New York *Tribune* and his abolitionist friends permission to
use the Smithsonian lecture room. It was not for political
purposes, he said. Mr. Greeley, also remembering the hot
debate on meteorology at the United States Agricultural
Society meeting, resolved to get even with Professor Henry.

In the meantime, Henry was leaving no stone unturned to
get an unbreakable grip on the weather. He and the Commissioner of Patents, Amos Mason, finally succeeded in getting the telegraph companies to agree to allow daily weather
reports to be sent to the Smithsonian. The Washington *Daily
Star* carried the first weather reports in 1857, based on these
telegraphic messages. No forecasting was done: *New York
clear, pleasant; Philadelphia, clear, cool; Washington,
cloudy, wind east.*

134

The Dred Scott decision was made, largely by that good friend of the Smithsonian and Joseph Henry, Chief Justice Roger Brooke Taney. It said that Negroes could not be citizens and that Congress could not prohibit slavery in the territories. Before the anti-slavery forces had recovered from that, there was a crushing depression.

Now the great clipper ships, for which Mat Maury had sought to make the ocean safe, started to fade out of business. Even the *Flying Cloud* could not get a cargo. Maury, still fuming over his mistreatment by the Retiring Board, paid no attention.

Neither did he pay attention to what was going on at the Observatory, or at the Depot of Charts and Instruments. He wanted his name cleared by that Retiring Board and he was determined to keep in the public eye by any means he could until that end was reached. He entertained lavishly, he met everyone, knew everyone, pulled every wire, and lobbied unceasingly to achieve his purpose.

Maury had a great deal of personal charm and warmth. Although very small he was far from insignificant. Handsome in a straight-featured way, very bald, with dark, curly straggles of hair around his collar, he spoke vivaciously and gestured frequently with his small, soft hands. He had an excellent sense of humor, and wit sparkled in his private conversation, but he wanted only to be taken as a savant, a man of letters, by the public. He spoke authoritatively and seriously when he mentioned any scientific matters, especially to congressmen and their powerful friends. He moved in the better circles, and let people know it. The *Physical Geography of the Sea* is flecked through with important names of ambassadors and statesmen who had interested themselves in him. He belonged to a family with "connections." He considered himself, reasonably, a personage. He made friends easily both in person and by a world-wide correspondence; he was much admired, if not universally. Continually widening his circle of friends, he pressured them all without letup, pestering everyone, and finally the President, with the consent of Congress, appointed him a commander on the active list, with no back pay, no apologies, no explanations.[3] He was more than pleased.

Then he began to complain about the Abolitionists' "agitating."

Over at the Smithsonian Joseph Henry was still smarting under the allegations of Samuel F. B. Morse. He understood how Morse felt, as if he had pounded his very soul into that telegraph instrument. Still, he couldn't let Morse call him a liar—him, Joseph Henry, scientist and first secretary of the Smithsonian. Finally, at his suggestion, the Board of Regents asked for an explanation of Morse's charges that Henry was falsely claiming credit for inventing any part of the telegraph.

"I can truly aver that I had no desire to arrogate to myself undue credit, nor to detract from the just claims of Mr. Morse," Henry said [4] in explanation of his own attitude, and then proceeded to demolish Morse's claims in short order. A committee appointed by the Board of Regents, with President Felton of Harvard as chairman, made a careful examination of all accessible evidence and concluded: *Mr. Morse's charges not only remain unproved, but they are positively disproved.*[5]

Mollified, Henry returned to scientific investigation again. Most of his writings of this period were on meteorology. Meanwhile, Commander Maury was making speeches on meteorology all over the then Northwest, of which Chicago was the largest city. It was in Cincinnati, however, that Maury spoke to the largest crowd. His daughter Nannie in her biography of him says [6]: *In this lecture Maury also paid just tribute to Mr. Morse, as the first inventor of the electric magnetic telegraph.*

While the Lincoln-Douglas debates were going on, Professor Henry and Professor Bache were more concerned with pulling down Commander Maury and his pretensions to grandeur by trying to prove that the neglected Naval Observatory should not be entrusted with the important matter of providing correct time for the nation. They should confine their timekeeping activities to the sea. A land-oriented group should provide a time standard for the nation. Among other projects, Commander Maury was trying to get the Coast Survey taken over by the Navy, so the fracas was by no means one-sided. Jewett, late of the Smithsonian library, was not napping when there were digs to be taken at Henry. Professor Gould of the Dudley Observatory got dragged in and for a while it looked as if a small matter of official time might well wreck both Naval Observatory and Coast Survey as everyone fought to prove everyone else completely wrong about everything. Finally, at the suggestion of Chief Justice Taney, who was now chancellor of the Smithsonian Board of Regents, the Coast Survey and the Smithsonian agreed to let the Naval Observatory be official timekeeper for the nation. It might have everything wrong with it, but as Taney pointed out to Bache and Henry,[7] they were the wrong people to be trying to set the matter straight, as they were not private citizens but closely allied in people's minds with the institutions which they represented. It might mean the end of scientific endeavor in Washington if they got involved in some scandal or came to harm. The Treasury Department kept the Coast Survey, the Smithsonian put another quarter million in the Treasury at 6 per cent, and the Naval Observatory, now the official source of Greenwich time, bumbled on its way.

John Brown's raid at Harpers Ferry took place the same

year, 1859, as Darwin's *Origin of Species* was published. Maury was thoroughly shaken up by both. All southerners had an understandable dread of a slave insurrection, so hanging John Brown was to the average southerner as right and necessary as killing a mad dog. To the abolitionists, hanging him was martyring a saint who died to make men free.

Suddenly seeing the need for patience, understanding, and concessions, Maury again took to the pen, this time to try to save his country. A gnat's squeak made as great an impression: he could get published only in areas that already agreed with all he had to say. Everyone's mind was made up. He wrote to important public figures and was ignored. Of course, he expected the North to make the concessions, because the South had the Constitution on its side. It wouldn't have made any difference if he had guaranteed that the South would stop agitating for the annexation of Cuba.

When he did get in print in 1859 he wished he hadn't, under the circumstances. The Baltimore and Ohio Railroad invited a number of prominent southern citizens and Yankee newspapermen to go on an excursion to celebrate the opening of their new line to Wheeling. The festive bottle was in plenty of evidence, and as the scenery sped past the windows the occasion grew more and more enjoyable. Commander Maury told of his brother John Minor's adventures on Nukahiva and how the old native king had offered him a princess for a wife if he'd stay there. Among his hearers was N. P. Willis, one of the fashionable writers of the day and a close member of the Paulding circle. His recollection of the events recounted by Maury left something to be desired on the score of accuracy. The *Home Journal*, over his signature, carried a lengthy description of the sedate Commander Maury's marriage, while a young sailor, to a princess of the Sandwich Islands. Maury had to laugh harder than anyone else or he never would have lived it down. The apology he requested was

138

not for himself, he said, but for the princess, who was a most respectable lady. Willis, obviously fearing a libel suit, wrote Maury a letter so fulsome in its praises as to be ludicrous. He also added, well aware of Maury's troubles, that he had secretly vowed his pen to Maury's cause. But the damage was done, and Maury's name no longer looked so brilliant to the public.

Joseph Henry, who could believe in God quite comfortably (and even be a pillar of the New York Avenue Presbyterian Church) without tying Him down to a folk legend on the subject of the creation of the earth, was delighted with the *Origin of Species*. For the first time naturalists had a claim to a science, and one based on inductive reasoning. That his very close friend Louis Agassiz, now head of the zoology department at Harvard, disagreed with Darwin violently mattered not a bit. He did accede to Agassiz and some of his preacher friends and agree not to come out in print praising Darwin, but he refused to write anything condemning him, and in those touchy times that was the same thing as saying you were on Darwin's side. Asa Gray, the Harvard botanist, another good friend of Henry, had long been a correspondent of Darwin and dared to applaud his theory openly. And how plainly mirrored in Darwin's work he could see the theories of Sir Charles Lyell, first learned in a survey camp in the Catskills from Amos Eaton. All the history of the earth told the same story: change. If he was worried about the changes taking place in his country, Henry never made mention of it.

Cyrus Field's 1858 Atlantic cable had failed after working for only a few weeks, and a great public furor resulted. A British writer "proved" no cable had ever been laid and that the whole thing was a hoax. Maury preferred not to mention it although letters he wrote in this period indicate he knew it could be made to work. A British concern, Glass Elliott and Company, had made the cable, following their successful design for one used crossing the English Channel. Maury had suggested to Field how the cable ought to be made, and now, after ignoring Maury and using the British cable, Cyrus Field wrote Joseph Henry asking how it should be made for their next attempt. Knowing that the previous attempt had failed, and that he had a great reputation in this field to guard, Henry hesitated to put himself out on a limb. Finally, after several pages of temporizing, he blurted out in a couple of lines a design generally the same as Maury's and the Glass Elliott one: twisted copper wire surrounded by gutta-percha. Field felt sure the cable was not at fault but actually it was, the core not being thick enough and the insulation too flimsy around it, and carelessly made at that. However, it was to be years before he could get to sea with another effort, and in that length of time Glass Elliott's cable was improved.[8]

In 1860 Abraham Lincoln was elected president. The disaffected southern states, with this proof that the rest of the country planned their destruction, began to prepare for disunion.

Dick, the eldest Maury son, picked this year to get expelled from the University and to get himself engaged to Susan Gatewood Crutchfield, a beautiful girl with money, social position, and influential relatives—and utterly no sense of humor. His parents gave him much good advice on both subjects, to which he paid no attention at all, naturally. Silent Nannie wrote him a most touching letter about his intended, saying not to leap into marriage too suddenly, that she had often felt his father would have been happier with someone else, although he assured her to the contrary. Poor Nannie—her idolized and worthless eldest son was to be but too happy with his Victorian prude of a wife: they thoroughly deserved each other.

Maury made a hurried trip to England that fall to protect the British copyright on *The Physical Geography of the Sea*, and while he was gone South Carolina seceded from the Union.

Henry was still on his meteorological bender. He wrote an article on the new Smithsonian anemometer which was installed on top of one of the towers with other wind- and weather-measuring devices. He went to visit Bache at one of the Survey base camps and had the usual good time that everyone had at the Baches'. Their camp was on a mountaintop surrounded by pines, the scattered tents like angular mushrooms sprouted up from the soft brown silent ground cover of pine needles, there was Rhine wine in long-necked bottles, the witty and gracious hostess acting as if hoopskirts were meant to be worn in the wilds, and when the work was over they would take a walk. By moonlight they would sit around and sing and play guitars, while here and there lamps glowed in tents where the maps grew day by day, where the instruments were kept in repair, and where Bache was rooting about in the medicine chest for something to relieve his strangely frequent headaches.

From there Henry went to Minot's Ledge to see the new lighthouse, out on the *Mistletoe* for some acoustic experiments, down to Princeton to pick up his family and bring them and some guests back to his redstone castle in Foggy Bottom. Their little white dog died, after frightening everyone by exhibiting symptoms of hydrophobia, and Henry felt as if one of the family had gone. He had forgotten how attached one could get to a pet.[9]

South Carolina had put on the secession act before, in 1831 Then, Andrew Jackson had moved swiftly and decisively, and Charleston had suddenly looked like an armed camp, her streets full of soldiers, her harbor full of warships, and peace had prevailed. Now Buchanan could only temporize. He knew his navy had been piddling around with new inventions such as screw propellers, side-wheelers, and fancy guns, while the fleet that was supposed to protect our shores had somehow faded away to nothing. Isaac Toucey, his Secretary of the Navy, was a southern appeaser, and he had kept what few ships the Navy had (five heavy screw frigates, all out of commission, seven screw sloops, eight second-class screw sloops, and four paddle-wheelers) [10] scattered all over the world so that the South could see the government planned no aggression against it. There were about eight ships of the United States Navy in home waters at this time. And the action of the Naval Retiring Board, in trying to promote Naval efficiency by removing the dead wood from the officer ranks, had been largely nullified by the political pull of the removees.

No ships, fumble-headed brass, and crews that hated steam and wanted the old sailing ships back—no wonder South Carolina could act so confidently. Her great harbor was perfectly safe. The Army, under General Winfield Scott, hero of a war with little Mexico, numbered some 16,000 soldiers, most of whom were on Indian-fighting duty on the frontier. Buchanan took to his prayers to save the nation, until he was out of the White House.

Maury tried to set up a convention of sober-minded men from both North and South who would air their grievances moderately, vote an apology to the South for angry utterances in the past, and, after guaranteeing slavery forever (and room for it to expand westward), smooth the way to reunion. Picking New Jersey as a median site for such a meeting, he wrote Governor Stockton and other border governors about the plan. They didn't even bother to answer.

Slightly shaken by this evidence of Yankee bad faith, Maury found himself now less set for conciliation. He began to compare the South's right to secede from the Union with that the colonies had exercised in casting off the yoke of British rule. The Constitution had not been framed for two sections with opposing interests, but for one country, he said.

142

Therefore the South, now outvoted by the North, should have
a veto power. The idea that the South should give up anything as a result of majority rule was unthinkable: evidence
of how the North hated the South and was jealous of it. It
would be better for the South, with dignity, to withdraw from
the unpleasant association.

Rutson Maury, Mat's rich tobacco-trader cousin in New
York, wrote him some plain Yankee-version truths. As he
saw it, the South always got the best of everything (the complaints about import duties he waved aside), and the Constitution was big enough for everybody. If everyone was willing to give in a little the fugitive-slave problem could still be
cleared up. This from a man who no doubt often had seen on a
northern street the innocent passers-by turned into an angry
mob by the sight of some wretched, manacled Negroes being
hauled off to a South-bound train by the police.

Rutson was, although none of them was prepared for it,
the Maurys' anchor in the trouble to come. He might occasionally seem a little too obviously laying up rewards in heaven,
but so desperately was his help needed that no one but the
impossible Dick ever told him off.

Joseph Henry's eldest daughter Mary, small and dark and
oval-faced like her mother, intelligent and kind, undeniably
an old maid even at twenty-three, now began to keep in earnest
the diary she had started in 1858. There are no secret con-
fidings in it, few mentions of her family, only the war as the
family in the Smithsonian saw it, from their windows, on the
public streets, in the daily papers. Her father's wartime official duties went into the now-lost Locked Book and are only
mentioned casually, as something that everyone knew about.
It is a plain, unpretentious telling, the reports of a young
woman watching a war which was happening right in front of
her and in which the conventions of Victorian life would not
allow her to take part.

Now, other states were leaving the Union in the wake of South Carolina. Mary Henry joined the throng in the Senate gallery to hear the valedictory speeches of the departing secessionist senators. Judah P. Benjamin's struck her most forcibly; in his most silvery tones he said it was too late, too late, to settle the differences between North and South. She came away depressed by the realization that her country was no longer united. It was some comfort to her, however, that they had a great many New Year's callers, among them Dorothea Dix.

The *Star* (now the Washington *Evening Star*, as it is today) was in the process of adjusting its editorial policy and the editor was clearly having difficulty deciding what course to advocate. In one issue he cautioned the public to avoid any overt act that might plunge the country into war; in another he urged the North to make concessions to the South; in still another he listed the "conquests" made by South Carolina, with Major Anderson besieged in Fort Sumter, and asked if this was peaceful, constitutional secession, or armed rebellion and open war against the United States? When at last Editor Wallach decided for the Union, defend it come what may, it was with reasonableness and decorum. The time for heated speeches would come to the *Star* before this fateful year of 1861 was out, but now Mr. Wallach, remembering the fate of the *National Era*, the late abolitionist newspaper in town, spoke his piece with moderation.

There were about three thousand slaves in Washington at this time,[11] and some 11,000 free Negroes; the unpaved streets were lined with big old elm trees, magnolia and crepe myrtle bloomed everywhere, the dogwood dropped its white stars on the early spring grass, and the black locust filled the air with its honeyed smell; fine blooded horses pranced by under saddle; the city sewers emptied into the open canal and

festered into notable, almost Parisian stinks; and everywhere
was the languor and idleness of the South. To the people from
the North and the West flocking into town for Lincoln's
inauguration, it was a distinct shock: their country's capital
was in the South! If it came to war, and there were hotheads
who said it would, this town would be surrounded by enemies.
Virginia, Maryland—why, even Delaware held slaves. And
every time they picked up the paper there was some new
disaster on the national scene.

As the town prepared for Lincoln's inauguration it was
obvious that under the busyness there was an agony of ap-
prehension.

The *Star* was very friendly toward Lincoln, reporting his
arrival in town with dignity and his stay at the Willard with
sense and good taste; it had recorded various of his speeches
en route to the capital as crowd charmers. There was near
despair in many hearts as they saw the gawky westerner in
whose hands was now held the future of the republic. The
Star's reassurance, its calm acceptance of Lincoln, helped
him a great deal. There was plenty to gossip about behind
the *Star's* stories, but, after all, it was only one sheet folded
in two, and there was plenty of local news to report in a pious
vein, as though trying to set the "tone" of the town. On February 25, 1861, the *Star* told how a standing-room crowd attended the exhibition at the Smithsonian of the pupils of the
Columbia Institute for the Deaf, Blind, and Dumb. Under
the direction of Professor Gallaudet, a little blind girl played
the piano, deaf children read lips and proved they understood
what was said to them by writing their replies on a blackboard, and the audience, torn between weeping and cheering,
applauded heartily. The New York *Tribune's* editor, Horace
Greeley, the *Star's* pet hate, arrived in town for the inaugural:
*His face looks as plump and fat as the body of a picked reed
bird in the height of the shooting season.* Spalding's Cephalic

145

Pills were guaranteed to cure sick headaches, nervous headaches, all kinds of headaches.

The Henrys had a house full of guests for the inauguration, among them John Bell of Tennessee, who had run for the presidency on the short-lived Constitutional Union party ticket.

Following the inauguration, the town settled down to a protracted case of nerves. Horace Greeley went back to New York; the *Star* snapped that he looked as happy as if he had a nail in his foot. On March 9 the *Star* reported that the President's first levee caused quite a jam. Lincoln wore the usual evening black, with white gloves, and had suave John Nicolay, one of his secretaries brought from Illinois, with him. Mrs. Lincoln, surrounded by female relatives, not all of them pro-Union, wore red watered silk with pearls. President Lincoln was estimated to have shaken hands at the rate of 1,500 an hour for two and a half hours, then went to bed exhausted, leaving his wife in charge of the party to which everyone in town that was white and decently clean was welcome to come. This was the famous crush where guests had to leave by the windows and no one could get his own wraps back from the cloakroom. Among the notable guests reported by the *Star* was "Capt." Matthew Fontaine Maury. The Henrys stayed home. Seven states had seceded.

Fort Sumter surrendered on April 13, 1861. They said that Edmund Ruffin, the white-haired, brilliant author of many books on scientific agriculture, yanked the cord that fired the first cannon aimed at the fort. Four years later he killed himself. But now the grim ball was opened, the great fiesta of death in which more American soldiers were to die than in any war before or since.

Washington succumbed to wild disorder. Secessionists danced in the streets. They flaunted their blue cockades and shouted that Washington would be the capital of the Southern

146

Confederacy. Lincoln asked for 75,000 volunteers [12] and the northern and western states' response reassured the panic-stricken loyal population, the telegraph fairly scorching with messages announcing quantities of promised men and equipment from governor after governor. Tensely, officials and citizens waited for them to arrive, knowing the only railroad ran through Baltimore, a town with a large population of toughs known for their secesh sympathies. Rumors spread like wildfire: a rebel army was poised just beyond Alexandria, ready to seize a defenseless Washington. Long Bridge was fortified at the Washington end, thirty-three militia companies were formed, including the Silver Greys who all had to be more than forty-five. James H. Lane, who had been military commander of the free-state troops in Kansas and elected senator from that unhappy territory, moved into the big East Room of the White House with a crowd of Jay-hawkers he called the Frontier Guard, ostensibly to guard Lincoln's person.

Virginia seceded on April 17, 1861.

Mary Henry wrote in her diary that they went up on the high tower of the Smithsonian and could see the secessionist flags over the buildings in Alexandria,[13] while the Stars and Stripes waved over the buildings in Washington. The sight of those flags so close, just across the river and a little farther down, affected Mary Henry more than the knowledge that the secesh mobs in Baltimore had torn up ("injured," she put it) the railroad tracks, pulled down the telegraph wires, and burned the railroad bridges. The New York papers were brought by Pony Express ("Latest California News by Pony Express" was one of the *Star's* columns), and there had been a one-day panic when Central Market had turned up deserted and food prices had skyrocketed. They were isolated from the rest of the country. Of the promised men and supplies only the Sixth Massachusetts had arrived, and they had lost four men killed to the Baltimore toughs. Harpers Ferry arsenal was lost, burned by Union men before they abandoned it. At least, everyone was repeatedly assured, Gosport Navy Yard at Norfolk was safe; on April 21 it was burned and abandoned.

Resignations from the Army, Navy, and government positions were numerous, embarrassingly so. The *Star* began to muffle the lists of names, frantically filling up space with the account of four wagonloads of hogs being removed by the police from those public wallows otherwise known as streets, and the arrest of one fellow for attempting to rescue his bacon before it could be carted off to the asylum and sold at auction. But now the names were so important since the defection of Virginia that the *Star* could not suppress them. On April 23, 1861, it announced as having resigned from the Army: [14] General Joseph E. Johnson, Quartermaster General; Colonel Robert E. Lee, 1st Cavalry; Lieutenant J. B. Hood, 2nd Cavalry; Colonel John B. McGruder, 1st Artillery. Over at the Navy Yard apparently almost everyone from Superintendent Franklin Buchanan on down had left, but the *Star* hurriedly assured its readers that they were not disunion; there had been a misunderstanding with the Army as to who had jurisdiction over the area and it was all a mistake.[15] Commander Maury was not mentioned.

Other papers mentioned him. He had resigned April 20, 1861. Everything seemed out of focus and bewildering. Many of Joseph Henry's best friends went South and left him. Most of Matthew Fontaine Maury's worst enemies went South with him, to be his superiors and critics.

NOTES TO CHAPTER EIGHT

1. They were unable to get started on this plan until after the Civil War.

2. Washington *Daily Star*, January 10, 1856.

3. All of which he had demanded as his "right."

4. Smithsonian Report of 1851, quoted in *Joseph Henry, A Memorial*.

5. *Ibid.*

6. *Matthew Fontaine Maury, U.S.N. and C.S.N.*, by Corbin.

7. Letters to Alexander Dallas Bache, September 28, 1858, and October 4, 1858. One of Henry's arguments against having Maury provide the correct time was that there was no assurance that it would be done correctly.

8. There is a display of these cables and other items dealing with the Atlantic cable at the Smithsonian.

9. Letters and papers of Joseph Henry at the Smithsonian.

10. *Picture History of the U. S. Navy*, by Roscoe and Freeman, and *A Compact History of the U. S. Navy*, Pratt.

11. I have a microfilm copy of the 1860 census for Washington, and a total of the separate slave schedules gives roughly this amount.

12. To serve for only three months.

13. With Mr. De Bust's telescope, surely.

14. With things the way they were in the country at this time no one dared resign any official post at all unless they wanted to be thought "secesh."

15. It was the *Star* that was mistaken.

CHAPTER NINE

Henry and the War in Washington (Part One)

As IF WHISKED away by one of John Quincy Adams' necro-mancers, the indolent southern town that had been Washington vanished. It vanished on April 25, 1861, with the cheers, the wild, hysterical cheers, with which the majority of its citizens poured onto Pennsylvania Avenue to meet the 7th New York Volunteer Infantry Regiment fresh from the cars [1] by way of Annapolis, steamboats, Perryville, half-abandoned branch lines, and many a roundaboutness. Even President Lincoln himself went out to wave at them, looking mightily relieved. Only that morning the town had seemed surrounded by the enemy, waiting to be picked off. Now a great wave of optimism and enthusiasm swept over it. Day after day the loyal states' volunteer regiments and those recruited by wealthy or determined private individuals poured into town. Cross-eyed militia General Ben Butler and his Massachusetts boys marched into Baltimore and took over the railroad depot, the yards, and the telegraph office. The secesh mob leaders were jailed, cannon were planted overlooking the town, and amid the resultant quiet the railroads operated without trouble, all those in and out of Baltimore being designated the "United States Military Route," the train schedules of which were published in the papers over the lines, *By order of the Secretary of War: Thomas A. Scott, Gen'l Manager.*

However, Washingtonians soon found their nerves acting up again. A hundred thousand frisky, spirited volunteers were quartered all over town and overflowed into every nook and cranny. Bugles blew and drums beat, and the measured tread of marching boots and crash of musketry practice and boom of artillery and clatter of horse-drawn gun carriages and cavalry outfits accompanied by barking dogs were heard from dawn till dusk. At night "the watchfires of a hundred circling camps" glowed about the town and the Provost's Guard patrolled the street futilely trying to enforce the nine-thirty curfew. Society fellows from the 7th New York flirted shamelessly with the wives and daughters of the local aristocracy, and helped provide the finest season of gossip anyone could remember. The First Zouaves, a regiment of toughs recruited from the New York volunteer fire departments by Elmer Ellsworth, and clad in uniforms of red and blue, shook up the rougher parts of town. The 75th New York, recruited by Col. Cameron, whose brother was Lincoln's first Secretary of War,[2] shook up everybody as they paraded with bare knees flashing under their kilts.

Alas, these brave young fellows openly sneered at sleazy Washington. There was no industry of any sort, the big buildings were mighty few and far between, the Capitol dome was mostly scaffolding, nobody had touched Washington Monument since the Know-Nothing riots of 1857 and its base stood lonely in a riot of unassembled marble parts in a cow pasture between where the Smithsonian grounds ended at Fourteenth Street and the river. The canal behind the shabby President's House was a dreadful fetid sewer that promised plague; the storm drain down Fourteenth Street broke during every violent rain and flooded the main business section; an abattoir and soap factory flourished in the Seventh Ward, adding to the canal's rich aroma, and nobody seemed to care. Bawdy houses flourished all over town; drunken fights, knifings, and shootings occurred continually, with riots to break the monotony of single combat. The citizens prayed to be delivered from their rescuers. There was one blessing: the hog nuisance was abated—those rowdy fire department Zouaves simply stole every porker they found around loose. The *Star*, calling them "Pet Lambs," cheered them on.

The atmosphere in Washington was that of a great volcano getting ready to explode. And everyone was cheerfully positive that when it did the Southern Confederacy would be as completely destroyed as Pompeii.[3]

The madness of the town spread to the redstone halls and quiet grounds of the Smithsonian in short order. Men with brilliant ideas, crackpots and swindlers, crowded in to see Joseph Henry all day, feeling him their gateway to government contracts and resultant riches. At least he listened to their stories. Some he was able to direct to Army and Navy officials to whom their signal lights and bread-making devices and explosive shot might mean something. One or two, such as T. S. C. Lowe, the young balloonist and a character in his own right, he encouraged and helped because he thought their ideas might shorten the coming conflict. For the government Henry was now serving as the only civilian on a committee of naval officers appointed to examine the so-called Stevens battery, a heavily-armed ironclad designed for harbor defense. The naval officers took one look and condemned it, but Henry, naturally, couldn't make up his mind. It was difficult to con-

153

centrate now, with all the noise there was around the Smithsonian, the heavy traffic on D Street South, which ran by the rear of the building, the rattle of muskets firing all day and part of the night at target practice on the grounds, bands playing, and the general disruption of the town.

Henry's son, Will, was twenty-five and unmarried, and worked at the New York Assay Office. He was frequently in Washington and often helped his father with work connected with the Smithsonian. With 100,000 volunteers camped in his home town he was in no hurry to volunteer himself. Mary, who wrote so assiduously in her diary of everything but the Henrys' daily life, was half talented: she had the ability to perform well in several fields of artistic endeavor, particularly sculpturing, but no drive, no ambition, no ability to concentrate. Her younger sisters, Nell, twenty-one, and Carrie, nineteen, were attractive, scatterbrained, and loathed the romantic Smithsonian and its isolated park. Even the excitement of uniforms couldn't make Washington attractive to them. They wanted to spend the summer with Uncle Stephen and his family and their friends at Princeton. Mrs. Henry was looking with worried eyes upon the legion of little boys, eight and ten years old, who supported themselves by selling newspapers.

Henry made an abortive duty call on Lincoln to present himself as representative of a charge of the President, the Smithsonian Institution. He found a man unkempt and ill at ease,[4] trying to cope with hordes of officeseekers, government contractors, wild-eyed inventors, Army, Navy, and Militia officers, department heads paying official calls, and the worries of a country disrupted and possibly headed for disintegration. Secretary of State Seward was with him. Henry did not stay. But at least he had the satisfaction of knowing, as he got into his buggy and drove off behind old Push, that the sympathies of the Smithsonian for the preservation of the

154

Union had been expressed. For Lincoln himself he had no sympathy, feeling him an opportunist politician, an uneducated, uncultured boor who could never understand the high aims of the Smithsonian.

Mary went with friends to visit the encampment of the dashing 7th, Washington's favorite regiment even if they had only enlisted for the requested ninety days (many of the volunteers were so carried away by the spirit of "Massachusetts agin Virginny" that they enlisted for three years), and admired their camp on a beautiful spot opposite Columbia College. Colonel Ellsworth, the young friend of Lincoln, who was working the fire department Zouaves into a well-disciplined group and making them like it, caught Mary's eye. He was short, fair, not handsome, humorous, physically strong, patient, and yet had an air of being completely defenseless. The tough Zouaves adored him to a man and he was the victim of a whispering campaign which said he knew how to handle these criminal types so well because he had once been one of them.

The Confederacy declared war on the United States on May 4, but there was no reciprocal action by the Union government of course. Lincoln's policy excluded any action that would accord the secessionists any status other than that of armed rebellion. Joseph Henry thought it would all surely end in a bloody battle. Not a war, a battle.

Horace Greeley, the pride of the abolitionists, began to feature a battle cry, "Forward to Richmond," in the columns of the *Tribune*. There was so much trouble with the soldiers in town that everyone was relieved when, on the night of May 23–24 (Virginia having ratified the Articles of Secession), 10,000 men were quietly marched through the moonlight across Long Bridge and the Aqueduct Bridge [5] to take up positions in Virginia. They were spoiling for a fight and fairly raced to seize the traitor soil of Virginia. Some were set to work building earthwork forts, some to fell trees across the roads to thwart cavalry raids, some to Alexandria to rout out any nests of rebels, and some wandered through the abandoned halls of the Custis-Lee plantation house, "Arlington," whose massive Doric pillars gleamed across the river overlooking Washington.

It was a quiet day, and they were contemptuous of things Confederate, for being so easily won, when a tremendous shouting and outcrying was heard from Alexandria. The fire department Zouaves had gone there, since that seemed the likely spot for trouble, and all were agog to see what desperate thing they had done now.

There was a three-story brick hotel in Alexandria, the Marshall House, of which one James W. Jackson was proprietor, and from the roof of which, naturally, was displayed the Confederate flag. Colonel Ellsworth had raced up the stairs, pulled down the flag, and had been shot and killed by Jackson as he came back downstairs carrying the flag. Private Brownell of the Zouaves promptly killed the hotel's proprietor with a musket shot.

The ardor for war and destruction burned more brightly than ever now that the young hero lay dead in the East Room of the President's House, the flags of the city at half mast, the bells of the fire departments tolling. He had worked in the Lincoln-Herndon law office in Springfield, and Lincoln had loved him as a son. This was the first sacrifice, one deeply felt by the people of the North who were not too proud to weep with the heartbroken Zouaves. Mary Henry joined the silent throng along Pennsylvania Avenue as the funeral procession passed by under flags tied with crape, noting with streaming eyes that the company of Zouaves walking behind the hearse was unarmed. One secesh remark and—well, it was better that way. Private Brownell carried the disputed flag, stained with Ellsworth's blood. Mary remarked in her diary that it was some consolation to know that Alexandria now lay under the Stars and Stripes.

While her father was trying to make up his mind to come out in favor of the Stevens battery in the face of such formidable opposition as the Navy presented, Mary and most of the other gadabouts in Washington were surfeiting themselves with a new hobby: visiting the camps. Passes were procured early in June from the Provost's Office for her to go with Professor Felton and Judge Loring's family to see "Arlington," the grounds of which Mary found indescribably picturesque. Like a true lover of all things Pickwick, she described the white tents of the soldiers as being set in "dingles." "Arlington" she described as the home of the descendants of Washington, and added that it was full of soldiers. The following day they crossed Long Bridge again with their passes and went to Alexandria and looked at the Marshall House. To their disapproval souvenir hunters had whittled away the stair rail and newel post, two stairs, a window, and the double front door. They took only part of the flagpole. Driving out beyond the town, they found fortifications commanding the roads to Manassas Gap and Fairfax Court House, and to Richmond. The Zouaves, the Pet Lambs, were immediately to the rear of the forts, having promised not to make a funeral pyre for their dead leader out of Alexandria.

There was excitement for Joseph Henry on June 18, 1861. Professor Lowe, his hydrogen-gas manufacturing apparatus and a large silk balloon with *Enterprize* on the side arrived at the Smithsonian. Joseph Henry had long been urging Lowe to offer his services for aerial reconnaissance and finally the young aeronaut arrived bag and baggage, to try to win over the armed forces' thinking on the subject, the direct way. A crowd gathered to watch the balloon inflated and after considerable wallowing and wiggling about if finally began to rise and then to tug at the ropes which held it down. Into the passenger basket underneath hopped the earnest balloon-ist, and to the delight of the rapidly-growing crowd the ropes were loosened and it rose to a height of several hundred feet. Lowe had carried a light telegraph wire with him and sent messages to an operator on the ground describing the beauties of the scenery. Pulled by a crowd of men and boys, it was moved to the grounds of the President's House, bobbing sedately along above the trees in the calm evening air. Later, installed on the grounds of the Armory, adjoining the Smith-sonian to the east, it was a popular curiosity for weeks and the public was allowed to ascend in it for a small fee.

The *Star's* reporter was so genuinely pleased with his jaunt (about like going up and down in an open-air elevator) that one wonders if he knew hydrogen was inflammable and that several of Lowe's predecessors had ascended to heaven in fiery chariots, as it were. It was proposed that this poten-tial flaming torch be taken into battle areas, regardless.[6] Henry had got Lincoln interested in the balloon as an aerial-reconnaissance medium but General Scott was a tougher nut to crack altogether. The President had to take Lowe per-sonally to Winder's Building across the Avenue in order to get Scott to talk to him.

Horace Greeley was reiterating the "Forward to Rich-mond" theme so vigorously that it was being taken up by other newspapers. On June 10 Union men had died to great headlines in a skirmish with the rebels at Big Bethel, near Yorktown, Virginia, the rebels winning. On June 3, at Phi-lippi, the Confederates had broken and run, to the great amusement of the Yankees, who referred to it as the Philippi Races. There was minor fighting in the West, all with thun-derous headlines. No one, it seemed, had any conception of what war was really like. It would be six weeks yet before they found out beside a quiet little stream called Bull Run.

Joseph Henry went to call upon President Lincoln in June

and found him vastly improved in appearance and manner. His conversation, somewhat obscured by his nervous anecdotal habit, was intelligent and forceful. And the expression at first thought coarse from being so vividly set forth in bold features Henry now found somehow arresting. Professor Felton, who had gone with him, propounded the virtues of the Smithsonian, while Lincoln and Henry looked at each other covertly and both began to change earlier opinions of the other.

Henry had been very pleased by Lincoln's naming Captain James Gilliss to take over the United States Naval Observatory. At last, after all these years, Gilliss was in charge of the project he had worked so hard to set up, and those with sterling hindsight said it should always have been so. He was looking for men with mathematical backgrounds to train as observers, with little luck. Henry remembered a young man who had come to see him recently with a new idea on the binomial theorem, so shy he had almost been frightened away by the janitor, admittedly self-taught, unassuming, yet so obviously talented that the professor had been quite drawn to him. He now recommended Simon Newcomb for the job.

More regiments poured into town. Tough gangs ventured forth from the disreputable Seventh Ward at night and prowled among the scavenging rats for easy pickings from drunk and solitary soldiers and from rich contractors waylaid as their buggies passed through the dark streets. Prostitution flourished and the madams paid small fortunes in protection money. Cooks and bakers were in great demand, according to the "Help Wanted" in the *Star*, with good wages and constant employment. Travelers coming into the capital from Virginia spoke of the great concentration of Confederate troops at Manassas Junction, thirty miles to the west. Some even saw two South Carolina companies within four miles of Alexandria. Engineers and draftsmen at the

159

Coast Survey, still working on their charts of the southern harbors and coast line at 1:30 A.M., were startled to see the night suddenly lit up; thinking the town was afire they ran to the windows to see the great comet of Charles V pass in pale glory across the sky. The *Star* began to refer to the soldiers as "Uncle Sambo's men." A flagpole was dedicated on the grounds of the President's House before a large crowd, the ceremony going off with éclat, the *Star* noted. The 12th New York was there with Wither's band, a group of regulars with the Marine Corps band, and Griffin's battery. After a prayer by the Reverend Smith Pine of St. John's, Lincoln raised the flag, the battery fired a 34-gun salute, the bands played martial airs, General Scott tottered out onto a veranda of the President's House, every loyal throat burst into nine cheers, and "enthusiasm reached a high point."

An extra session of Congress having been called, the Henrys went to see the opening, Mary devoting most of her attention to noting who was not there, although by this time her father was pretty well won over to Lincoln both as man and president. The activities of this session met with the approval of the *Star*, which thought that the passage of bills providing for half a million men and half a billion dollars spelled an end to "the attempt to erect over the South an oligarchic despotism." Success for the Union was foreseen, though with a word of caution: "If the government can successfully restrain its own soldiery, so that they shall perpetrate few or no outrages upon private individuals or property wherever they progress triumphantly, the masses will gladly return to their allegiance, so soon as satisfied that the government possesses the strength requisite to defend them successfully from the vengeance of the oligarchy, and aims simply to restore to them their lost rights, liberties, privileges, and property as citizens of the United States." [7]

A young general named McClellan was with a Union force

160

in what later became West Virginia, the officers under him racking up victory after little victory for which he took full credit. At Rich's Mountain, "Billiards" Pegram had to surrender, and Richard Ashby was killed at Carrick's Ford. The headlines played it up: *Gen. McClellan's Victory complete! Pegram's Route Complete! He is Overtaken and Surrenders With the Remnant of his Troops! Gen. McClellan now has One Thousand Prisoners, with all their Artillery, Baggage, Wagons, Tents, etc., even to their Tin Cups!* The Federals' only problem was how to handle the prisoners. Were they to be regarded as captured soldiers of a belligerent army, or as caught rebels liable to hanging? No one knew.

"Forward to Richmond!" shouted the out-of-town papers.

On July 16 the Henrys again climbed to the top of the high tower of the Smithsonian, this time to watch the troops start out for battle. Mary Henry heard their enthusiastic shouts, and found it very sad to watch them go. *I could not feel patriotic*, she wrote in her diary that night.[8] But the *Star's* reporter found it the most sublime spectacle he had ever seen, regiment after regiment marching away, those already across the river and those crossing Long Bridge meeting at the tollgate and proceeding on together, the colorful uniforms, the joyous shouts, the bands playing, the *vivandiers* with their canteens, the long, white-sheeted wagon train, all aglitter in the summer sun. Perhaps he wished he could be going, too: *The enthusiasm and elasticity of spirit of the troops ordered to march, their jokes with brother soldiers, their boyish naïveté and abandon, were infectiously joyous.*

Fairfax Court House they found abandoned. The 14th New York (the Brooklyn regiment), to teach the rebels a lesson, burned the largest house in town; the owner, a loyal unionist, threatened to have them all hanged. General McDowell's official dispatches were printed in the *Star*. Little wonder that Rose Greenhow had no difficulty getting all the federal plans and sending them to Confederate General Beauregard in time for him to order Johnson to reinforce him. The Federals, bivouacked this night at Fairfax, thought Beauregard alone at Manassas. The *Star's* special correspondent wrote that they expected to find Centerville had been evacuated during the night; *We shall have turned Manassas Junction, too, by Friday forenoon or I am much mistaken,* he added. The Confederate withdrawal he sarcastically labeled *A brilliant retrograde movement upon Manassas.*

With a major battle clearly in the offing, the *Star* paused to castigate Matthew Fontaine Maury on July 19, 1861:

The Humbug Maury turned up again. Submarine batteries. *Under date of June 9, the Norfolk correspondent of the Richmond Examiner says, "Capt. Maury, late of the Washington Observatory, left here this morning. It is understood that he has been planting in the approaches to this city some of the most formidable submarine batteries. They will be quite a match for any iron-plated ships which the enemy can bring. The like are to be planted in all our rivers, so as to render our cities and our people perfectly secure against any approaches by water."*

In the city of Washington Capt. Maury is so thoroughly appreciated that no invention purely of his own will be likely to receive much consideration. His career, when those qualified to do it justice shall undertake to depict it, will exhibit one of the most remarkable and successful careers of unblushing charlatanism known in the world's history. The impudence with which he seized and appropriated as his own discoveries of more able but more modest men than himself, like Prof. Henry, Prof. Espey, and others, was truly sublime in its colossal brazen front, and merits, what it has failed to receive heretofore, from his social relations and his high government position, a proper and truthful exposition. These

162

filchings, dressed up in a style of popular clap-trap, and industriously circulated by him through Europe, *served to give him a foreign reputation which he had trickster adroitness enough to perceive would react upon the American mind. The only feather amidst his jackdaw plumes believed to be legitimately his is the theory that sun-flowers are a chills and fever disinfectant.*

With the charlatan and trickster disposed of, attention could be refocused on the necessary chore of spanking the rebel army.

Carriages full of civilians, ladies, members of Congress, the wealthy, the pseudo-intellectual, the famous, the curious, all of them unthinking, drove out to Virginia to see the Confederates defeated—the Southern Races, they called it. Laughing, their picnic hampers stowed under the seat, their opera glasses polished, they went to enjoy the day as they had other jolly Sunday outings.

It was July 21, 1861.

General Winfield Scott was in touch with his troops by telegraph, and from the downstairs telegraph office in the rickety old War Department building came news of the battle at last, by the steep-banked stream called Bull Run, just north of Manassas Junction. The *Star* printed stunned repetitions of *A Battle at Bull Run! A number of the Federal Forces wounded if not killed! An Engagement is Probably in Progress at Manassas Junction!* Said the local news column: *We hear a thousand different rumors—one saying that expresses have reached here for all the physicians to be had to repair at once to Manassas to attend our wounded there, representing as numbering, with the dead, thousands. This is a lie of the first water.*[9]

Washington, so rackety of late, fell into a more-than-Sunday silence. Crowds gathered on Pennsylvania Avenue, waiting to hear the triumphant hoofs of victorious Confederate cavalry. "What happened? What happened?" came in anguished whispers. Lincoln and his cabinet met with General Scott to get the news together as over and over the telegraphers scribbled, *Retreat*. At last they understood it was a complete rout, that all was lost, that they must look to themselves to save Washington. "What *happened?*" All night the crowds stood waiting on the Avenue; a soft summer rain began, and after an agony of waiting came the dawn of defeat.

Through the steadily increasing downpour the Union army came back from Manassas. Only it was no longer an army; it was the shattered pieces of an army that had broken up on the field of battle and could not re-form. All day and all night ambulances passed the rear of the Smithsonian. The Rhode Island Regiment came in together at 10 A.M., but they were obviously worn out, filthy, many with no shoes, helping each other. All day troops straggled into the shabby town, which never before had looked so good, exhausted, hungry, in rags, soaking wet, weaponless, not knowing where to go or what to do, collapsing in doorways and sidewalks in the rain, cavalry asleep on their horses, the walking wounded huddled against the buildings, all needing help of one kind or another.

The loyal people of Washington rallied to their aid, the government buildings were opened for them, private residents took them in, even the National Rifles (who had been suspected of being pro-secesh) went out and brought them into Temperance Hall where there were cots and blankets and hot coffee. But there were still secessionists in the town, and more than a few. Some plainly showed their exultation. The *Star* waxed bitter: *Their inhuman joy at the suffering of the wounded soldiers as they passed our streets to the hospitals was the most reprehensible feature of their traitorous demonstration. The parties most conspicuous for their secession*

164

sympathies were precisely those from whom better things should have been expected. In obvious knowledge that their readers would know whom they were talking about, the *Star* went on: *Well-known jewelers, bankers, wood dealers, dry goods dealers, Criminal Court lawyers, magistrates, court criers, assistant market clerks, grocers (who furnish army stores).*

For days there was little in the *Star* but Bull Run. *The fight of yesterday is of course the subject of much criticism; as well it may be, for from beginning to end it was marked by circumstances that reflect little credit on those implicated in them. . . . The Army of the Potomac will be immediately re-organized.* Who started the retreat, and who stopped it, were much discussed. The civilian onlookers, many of whom perforce shared the unhappy flight of the soldiers, were accused of causing the initial panic. Long casualty lists were printed, as were rendezvous points for stragglers to report to for the various regiments, with the notice that all who failed to do so would be arrested. Finally someone got around to blaming Horace Greeley for the debacle.

But the Confederate army, as demoralized by victory as the Union army by defeat, fell apart nearly as spectacularly. So now there was assurance of a long war, and a bloody war.

With the big fight out of its system Washington settled down to train troops. McClellan was in charge now, and the militia colorfulness vanished under his insistence on discipline. Although it was still obviously an armed camp, with those thick-crowded white tents by day and watchfires by night on the low hills encircling the town, a marked sedateness, a certain businesslike air, now predominated. No dirty-shirt blue was seen idle in street or tavern, and Mary Henry noted with her childlike attachment to the old *status quo* that even *officers* had to have passes to come to town. The war was never to be out of their minds as long as it lasted, but after Bull Run Washingtonians felt less involved personally with the movements of the Army of the Potomac.

As the number of Joseph Henry's meetings with Lincoln increased so did his attachment for the rawboned Westerner. He realized that behind the humorous, self-deprecating front was a man who saw the most involved matters in all their ramifications, in their smallest implications. It was something of a shock when at last it was forced upon one that this crude fellow, this rustic, was a genius at intrigue and had such a subtle knowledge of people that he could use them to his every advantage. Having learned to swallow pride, to accept jibes and sneers without bitterness, Lincoln could smile, to himself, at his detractors. It must have been difficult for him, the master of foxes, to understand Joseph Henry. How he must have waited for the dignified professor to slip, to reveal himself the hidebound pedant. But as time went on it became more clear that Joseph Henry was just what he appeared to be, simple, sincere, honest, always direct and unassuming. A man such as Lincoln could relax around Joseph Henry and, sometimes, delight in teasing him.

Before the lamps were lit one quiet evening in this first summer of the war, Henry was sitting talking with Lincoln in his office as the day cooled off and the fireflies began to wink and the katydids sang in the broad lawns beyond the tall, open windows. Suddenly there was a commotion in the anteroom. One of the President's secretaries came in, apologetic, with a message for Lincoln that a strange man was outside who insisted on seeing the President on a matter involving the nation's security.

"Show him in," Lincoln said resignedly, motioning for Henry to keep his seat.

The gentleman caller, a prosperous citizen of the town,

was embarrassed but had obviously steeled himself to see the matter through.

"Mr. President, last night I was passing along beside the canal in my carriage and I happened to see a light in the tallest tower of the Smithsonian. It was very plainly winking out a message, probably to secesh in Virginia. That Professor Henry is secesh. Everybody knows it."

Lincoln, having difficulty with his voice, said, "Professor Henry, how do you explain this?"

The caller almost panicked as the tall scientist stood up suddenly in the gloom.

"Was this about nine o'clock?" Henry asked courteously.

"Ye-yes."

"That must have been Henry Horan, the night watchman, reading the meteorological instruments on the tower," he went on calmly. "He carries a lantern, and it was probably the sight of that passing back and forth in front of the open fretwork that you saw."

The flustered visitor obviously wished he was somewhere else, but Henry went on to assure him that he admired him for doing his duty, that it was the obligation of every citizen to report suspicious matters. Finally the poor man, still stuttering, made a thankful exit.

Lincoln, who had been making distressing noises during Henry's kindly speech, burst out in roars of laughter.[10]

Henry stood smiling gently at the tired president. He could almost find it in himself to love the man. Sometimes he had to remind himself to put on the brakes, so close a hold did Lincoln have on his emotions.[11]

It was no use, however, for Joseph Henry to tell his wife and daughters he had changed his mind about the prairie lawyer and now admired him. They clung to their attitude, the one common to the majority in Washington, that Lincoln was a totally incompetent boor. They saw his as an unenviable place in history, the one who would have to take the blame for the war.[12]

In October, as the armed town grew to accommodate nearly 240,000 soldiers and the war was spluttering along like a wet fuse from skirmish to skirmish, Simon Newcomb joined the Navy with the rank of professor (this was an actual naval rank of the time), and went to work at the Naval Observatory. Henry came to see how he was getting along, and was shown around by Gilliss and his new observer, then stayed for tea at the superintendent's house with his charming family, his visits being considered social and to be shared with all.

Work at the Observatory was conducted informally, to say the least. Gilliss didn't know what to do about the fact that the observers were used to doing as they pleased; his good-natured soul couldn't bring itself to straighten them out. The equipment was so antiquated and unreliable that they were all ashamed to think how poor a showing their work made to foreign astronomers.

In his book *Reminiscenses of an Astronomer*, Newcomb, the most broadminded and forebearing of men, was kind to the departed Maury, as he was to everyone, but the picture he presented of the Naval Observatory when he went to work there on October 7, 1861, was an odd one:

> Professor Yarnell, whose assistant I was, was an extremely pleasant gentleman to be associated with. Although one of the most industrious workers at the Observatory there was nothing of the martinet about him. He showed me how to handle the instrument and record my observations. There was a Nautical Almanac and a Catalogue of Stars. Out of these each of us could select what he thought best to observe.
>
> The custom was that one of us should come on every clear evening, make observations as long as he chose, and then go

home. The transit instrument was at one end of the building and the mural circle, in charge of Professor Hubbard, at the other. He was weak in health, and unable to do much continuous work of any kind, especially the hard work of observing. He and I arranged to observe on the same nights; but I soon found there was no concerted plan between the two sets of observers. The instruments were old-fashioned ones, of which mine could determine only the right ascencion of a star and his only its declination; hence to completely determine the position of a celestial body, observations must be made on the same object with both instruments. But I soon found there was no concert of action of this kind. Hubbard, on the mural circle, had his plan of work; Yarnell and myself, on the transit, had ours. When either Hubbard or myself got tired, we would "vote it cloudy" and go out for a plate of oysters at a neighboring restaurant.

Now in the previous history of the observatory, the astronomers fell into the habit of every one not only making his observations in his own way, but reducing them himself.[13]

In justice to Captain Gilliss it must be said that he was not in any way responsible for this lack of system. It grew out of the origin and history of the establishment. . . .

Maury, although (as he wrote a few years later) quite without experience in the use of astronomical instruments,[14] went at his work with great energy and efficiency, so that, for two or three years, the institution bid fair to take a high place in science. Then he branched off into what was, from a practical standpoint, the vastly more important work of studying the winds and currents of the ocean. . . . The new work was so absorbing that he seemed to have lost interest in the astronomical side of the establishment, which he left to his assistants. The results were that on this side things fell into the condition I have described, and stayed there until Maury resigned his commission and cast his fortunes with the Confederacy. Then Gilliss took charge and had to see what could be done under the circumstances.

It soon became evident to him that no system of work of

the first order of importance could be initiated until the instrumental equipment was greatly improved. The clocks, perfection in which is almost at the bottom of good work, were quite unfit for use. The astronomical clock with which Yarnell and I made our observations kept worse time than a high-class pocket watch does today. The instruments were antiquated and defective in several particulars. Before real work could be commenced new ones must be procured. . . . The personnel was as defective as the instruments. On it devolved not only the making of the astronomical observations, but the issue of clocks and chronometers to the temporarily immense navy. In fact, the observatory was still a depot of charts for the naval service and continued to be such until the Hydrographic Office was established in 1866.

In 1863 Gilliss obtained authority to have the most pressing wants supplied by the construction of a great transit circle by Pistor and Martins in Berlin. He had a comprehensive plan of work with this instrument when it should arrive, but deferred putting any such plan in operation until its actual conception.

As Henry was leaving they all paused in the entryway to the Observatory building to shake their heads over Locke's electro-chronograph, which Maury had gotten installed and had once been so proud of: *A large, marble-cased clock which . . . had acquired some celebrity for being supposed to embody the first attempt to apply electricity to the recording of astronomical observations. It was said to have cost a large sum, paid partly as a reward to its inventor. Its only drawbacks were that it did not keep time and had never, so far as I am aware, served any purpose but that of an ornament.*[15]

Joseph Henry, as he drove away down Pennsylvania Avenue behind the ancient Push, would have been justified in feeling proud of the help he had given to so many of the struggling young scientists of his time, some of whom, like young Newcomb, bid fair really to amount to something. But

170

his was so generous a nature that he never thought anything about it, except to make sure that he was always accessible to everyone. He and the others were there to spread that knowledge that was the hope of man for this world. They must guard against the academic hidebound attitudes found in so many long-established institutions. Old Peake, the janitor, wrote a guide to the Smithsonian; it was right and proper that he should.

Henry and a number of others were worried over a problem that involved the security of the country most seriously. There was a shortage of niter, one of the main components of black powder. Almost all niter had to be imported from India, under British rule, and the British were protesting the federal blockade of the southern coast, claiming that it was illegal and would operate to the detriment of their vast cotton-manufacturing industry. In fear that they might try to do something about it, Lammot Du Pont went to England in the fall of 1861 and hurriedly bought up all the available niter in the country, more than four million pounds. His was one of the large powder-making concerns in the country, and Du Pont knew what he was doing. While it was being loaded, however, the British government proclaimed an arms embargo, and the niter was removed from the American ships and stored in locked warehouses.

Cause of it all was Charles Wilkes, U.S.N., late of the Exploring Expedition and with one court-martial under his belt, who had been put in command of the fast propeller steam sloop *San Jacinto* and sent to search for Confederate blockade runners and privateers. Hearing in the Bahamas that the Confederate commissioners to England and France, James M. Mason and John Slidell, had gotten safely through the blockade to St. George, Captain Wilkes instantly made for the Bahama Passage and lay in wait for the British steamer *Trent*, bound for Halifax, which according to reports would be carrying the two commissioners. When the *Trent* appeared in the offing the *San Jacinto* fired across her bow. The blue flag with its white square in the middle was flown to indicate that this was a Royal Mail steamer, but another shot was fired from the rapidly-closing *San Jacinto*. The astounded British captain heaved to, a ship's boat full of Marines came aboard, and Messrs Mason and Slidell, their secretaries and papers, were forcibly removed.

Mason and Slidell were imprisoned in Fort Warren near Boston and Captain Wilkes walked the streets to cheers and huzzahs. He was the man of the hour, to the public. Official Washington, after an initial cheer, began to entertain sober second thoughts. Lord Lyons, the British ambassador, it was rumored, had begun to pack his portmanteau. The desire to tell England to go fly a kite had never been so tempting, but the possibility of war with England had never been so little to our liking. Fortunately, when the British note came it was moderate enough to afford the administration in Washington an easy way out. The federal government said it had all been a mistake: Captain Wilkes had acted entirely on his own initiative. Wilkes was court-martialed, found guilty, reprimanded, and returned to duty. In six months he was a rear admiral and back at sea again. However, the embargo on niter, lead, and arms was *not* removed.[16] Fortunately, though, potassium nitrate, the niter they had been using for gun powder, was not the only material that could be mixed with sulphur and charcoal to make the big bang. Sodium nitrate could also be used. Information at the Smithsonian showed vast deposits of this in Chile. Soon the stockpile of niter was in the millions of pounds and one more wartime emergency was solved. Back in 1857, Joseph Henry had urged the Secretary of War to finance research into finding substitutes for niter, to no avail.[17]

The Civil War issues of the *Scientific American* were full

of fascinating sidelights on the progress of the war, one page
in each being devoted to the fighting. Professor Henry, the
distinguished savant and director of the Smithsonian Institution, was frequently mentioned as being the only civilian
in the group assigned to inspect the Stevens battery. The
progress of building something called the Ericsson battery
was followed closely; this floating battery, when launched,
would bear the name *Monitor*. The Spencer breech-loading
rifle was also much discussed, diagrams showing how it worked
and confuting those who claimed it was too complicated. That
it was a weapon which might be copied advantageously by
the Confederates seemed to occur to no one. The use of cavalry
in battle was decried, the swiftest horse being no match for
the soldier with a rifle; what the army would use for reconnaissance the paper did not suggest. The transfer of Secretary of War Cameron to the job of ambassador to Russia
met with no complaints. The British were assailed regularly,
apparently because they had been stealing American patents.
The Ericsson battery neared completion: *The Ericsson iron-
plated floating battery at Green Point has been armed with
two 11-inch Columbiads, which have been furnished with 400
wrought-iron round shot, each ball costing $47 and weigh-
ing 184 pounds. These balls were made by forging square
blocks of iron at the Novelty Works, then turning them in the
lathe. Cast-iron shot are liable to break in pieces when fired
against thick iron plates. These wrought-iron shot are for
smashing through the sides of such secession floating batteries
as the* Merrimac, *at Norfolk, and* Hollin's Turtle *at New
Orleans.* An account of bad meat furnished the troops bore
the headline, *Hang the Rascals,* in reference to the contractors.

On February 5, 1862, a private party for 1,000 guests
was held at the President's House. All guests were required
to show their invitations at the door before they were ad-

mitted. It seems to have been the affair of the season. Mary Henry, who attended with her parents, ecstatically wrote in her diary that it was a *brilliant* party and that *everyone* was there. The President and Mrs. Lincoln received standing in the center of the much-used East Room, Mrs. Lincoln wearing white satin with black lace flounces half a yard wide festooned up with black and white ribbons, pearls, a Parisian headdress, and carrying a bouquet of crape myrtle. The Marine Band played, although there was no dancing, out of regard for the troubled times. A New York caterer, Maillard, had prepared the buffet and it was a stunner, the center and side tables covered with Greek helmets, Chinese pagodas, cornucopias, fountains, birds on their nests, a temple surmounted by the goddess of liberty, the good ship *Union* in full sail, and a dozen other marvels, all made out of sugar. They contained what the *Star* called "chicken fixin's," charlotte russe, "a superb pâté de foie gras" and other delicacies. The punch bowl held twenty bottles of champagne spiked with rum and was set on a table covered with sandwiches, biscuits, and cheese. The gala affair did not break up until three o'clock in the morning.

Upstairs eleven-year-old Willie Lincoln tossed in a feverish nightmare. Two weeks later he was dead of typhoid. It was to be a long time before another party was held in the Executive Mansion.

Professor Henry had Horace Greeley and the abolitionists on his neck again. After some initial trouble with Greeley and the meteorology scheme, he had been attacked by the *Tribune* for refusing to allow the lecture room at the Smithsonian to be used for abolitionist harangues. Henry was not to be moved from his position that political speeches were in direct violation of the rules and kept on turning the abolitionists down. So Mr. Greeley and his friends laid a trap for Henry.

A "front" group appeared at the Smithsonian, asking to use the lecture room, quite the finest in town, for a series of talks on popular subjects sponsored by the newly-formed Washington Lecture Association. Emerson and a couple of other well-known persons were named as speakers, and Henry was glad to agree. The speech on "Patriotism" turned out to be applied to immediate emancipation. The one on "The Conduct of the War" was abolitionism, pure and simple. Realizing he had been taken, Henry was all for canceling the rest of the series. Bache and others persuaded him not to do anything so conspicuous, since he was still suspected of secessionist sympathies. At the beginning of each abolitionist session, the chairman would state that the Smithsonian was not responsible for any statements made by the Washington Lecture Association, invariably adding some sarcastic comment to which Henry was powerless to retort. When Horace Greeley came to talk and Lincoln was in the audience (Greeley being a power in the Republican party), the Lecture Association disclaimed any responsibility for the Smithsonian Institution, to whoops of glee from the audience. After the lecture Lincoln stopped in at the Henrys' suite on the upper floor of the east wing and teased Joseph about Greeley's "getting" him.

Mary Henry waxed wrathy in writing in her diary about all this and even the *Star,* in reporting the affairs, seemed to be sympathetic with Henry. It complained on January 25, 1862: *Mr. Curtis's lecture was listened to with great interest, and all who heard him would gladly hear him again, upon some subject not political. Cannot the Lecture Association manage it? We have had now eight abolition lectures in succession: a "popular course" ought to show a little more variety.* A day or so later it reported that so enormous a crowd had attended the talk by Dr. Hays on his Arctic explorations at the Smithsonian that hundreds had been turned away

—and this when there were five vaudeville shows in town, and *Camille*. The Lecture Association apparently got the message: the abolition sentiment was considerably toned down thereafter and completely missing in some of the final lectures.

All this time there had been abuilding at the Confederate-held Gosport Navy Yard the ironclad *Virginia*. When the navy yard at Norfolk had been lost to the Confederates by sheer stupidity, the new United States steam frigate *Merrimac* had been burned by Hiram Paulding as the only way to prevent her falling into their hands. Now raised, with sloping iron covered decks above the water line like the scorned Stevens battery, and renamed, she was rumored ready to put to sea. The military telegraph operators were frantically laying an underwater cable from Fortress Monroe to Cape Charles so that Lincoln and the federal command in Washington could keep up with her actions by telegraph through the Eastern Shore and Maryland. The Ericsson battery, now named the *Monitor*, looked like the gadget-ridden daydream of a crackpot inventor; even those who wanted to believe in her found it difficult. The plans had been published in the *Scientific American*, where anyone who was interested could read a description of how the turret revolved: *The principal novelty of this vessel is the cylindrical revolving turret in which the guns are placed. This is formed of rolled one-inch iron plates bolted together to the thickness of eight inches; its internal diameter is 20 feet and it is nine feet high. It rests on its lower edge on a smooth, flat ring of composition metal, but when in action the principal portion of its weight is sustained by a central shaft, about which it revolves. . . . A large spur wheel upon the shaft is connected by a train of gearing with a small steam engine, which supplies the power for turning the turret.*[18]

The steam tug *Seth Low* got the "Yankee cheesebox on a

raft" down to Hampton Roads, thanks to an abatement in the wind that kept her from sinking with her whole crew of volunteers, and turned her loose to anchor beside the *Minnesota*, "hard and fast aground." [19] Daylight on Sunday, March 9, 1862, found the *Virginia* and her escorts off Sewall's Point. The *Cumberland* was gone with hundreds of her crew, the *Congress* had blown up in a series of explosions between one and two that morning, and here was the *Minnesota* aground and helpless. In Washington a government and a populace, presumably hardened to threats of danger, almost panicked. The *Virginia's* attack on the federal ships in Hampton Roads had been such an easy victory: everything the federals threw at her had bounced off and everything she had attacked was lost. The cable wasn't finished and all the news had to come by dispatch boat up the Potomac under the fire of Confederate gun emplacements, or to Baltimore and thence by telegraph. Washington actually expected the slanting shot-proof walls of the *Virginia* to appear in the Potomac; then the town would be destroyed by her gunfire.

"The *Virginia* couldn't get past Kettle Bottom Shoals," said someone hopefully.

"The traitor Maury took the charts of the Potomac River shoals with him when he went South," another replied, repeating the current gossip.

It was not until evening that the cable was completed, the people working on it almost too upset with happiness to be able to do their job, and Assistant Secretary of the Navy Gustavus Fox wired the good news to Lincoln that the tiny *Monitor* had stopped the great *Virginia*, and Hampton Roads was under Union control.

The Henrys' friend Franklin Buchanan, one-time superintendent of the Washington Navy Yard, was in command of the *Virginia*. Henry was glad he had at last approved the plan of the Stevens battery, although it had been difficult in the face of so much naval opposition. The Stevens battery it-self, despite his vote of confidence, had been sold to the French government. Now a whole fleet of ships on that radical plan, in imitation of which the *Virginia* had been built, were or-dered, and many river-going steamboats were to be converted to ironclads or timber clads on the same plan. Ships on the *Monitor* plan were of course also ordered.

The war began to look up. The Confederates withdrew their guns from the Potomac, and were found to have aban-doned Manassas also. McClellan was finally in the mood to advance on Richmond the roundabout way, by water, and took off to besiege Yorktown. Mary Henry, after having to take the oath as a loyal citizen, was permitted by the provost marshal to go to Alexandria to watch the shiploads of troops go by on their way down-river. She noticed how different they were from the way in which they had gone off to Bull Run, then with pranks and laughter, now serious and determined. Missing besides the smiles were the women hangers-on, the vivandières. With McClellan was Professor Lowe, three bal-loons, and the balloon tender *Coeur de Leon*, the first air-craft carrier, as it were.

McClellan could not get up the James past the batteries on top of the bluff at Drewry's Landing. The only one of his ironclads that could elevate its guns that high, the miniature of the Stevens battery called the *Naugatuck*, had one of its guns burst and was put out of commission. The river was full of artificial obstructions, and there were rumors of that in-vention of the devil, the submarine mine or torpedo, being planted in the river.

The mines were linked with the traitor Maury, and every-one was deathly afraid of them. However, the *Scientific Amer-ican* said on June 7, 1862: *We are well aware that the efforts in this line have been ridiculous failures—even the latest and most ingenious devised by the rebels in this war.* But nobody knew when the rebels might succeed in getting the infernal machines to work efficiently so the Yankees moved gingerly about in southern waters, expecting any moment to go up in a watery explosion.

Stonewall Jackson began to cavort about the Shenandoah, his infantry performing incredible feats of both marching and fighting. There was a Union victory at Shiloh, or Pittsburg Landing, and Grant began to come to the fore, although it was a sad victory, with 10,000 lost on each side. New Orleans was occupied after a fierce naval battle, and General Butler, who had tamed Baltimore so efficiently, was put in charge. Unfortunately he treated the respectable people of New Orleans the same way he'd treated the water-front riffraff in Baltimore and fanned the southern hatred of all things Yankee to an even higher pitch.

McClellan, once in the field, proved loath to do battle. Professor Lowe went up in his balloon at night near Yorktown and saw by the light of the campfires the area being evacuated. This he reported to McClellan's headquarters.[20] Not the following day, but the next, McClellan and his forces set out to take Yorktown—and somehow were surprised to find the earthworks empty, the whole point of land abandoned. After moving on cautiously for a bit the brass had to sit down and think about it. Jackson had slipped out of the trap the Union forces had laid for him up in the Shenandoah and was helping to defend Richmond. Professor Lowe, his balloon securely held down by a dozen soldiers all hanging on to its mooring rope, made reconnaissance flights and telegraphed back what he saw by his trailing telegraph wire. He was great at reporting cooking fires and movements over open roads and fields. But the peninsula before Richmond is almost unbroken forest. Most of the roads were so narrow as to be like tunnels through the trees. The dense growth of the swamp does not reveal even the Chickahominy from the air.

After a series of bloody battles McClellan withdrew to the area around the beautiful old house at Harrison's Landing,[21] and cried for more men, more supplies, more support. He had won engagement after engagement before Richmond, but the Confederates had saved their capital. Finally, burning millions of dollars' worth of supplies, blaming everyone for getting him into what was the most favorable situation a Yankee general was to see for quite a while, McClellan took his remaining 70,000 men back to Washington.

In a pig's eye that great army couldn't take Richmond, disgusted Yankees cried. They clashed with the Rebels at Bull Run again and were soundly trounced. McClellan had left; now McClellan came back.

Washington was like a vast hospital. Until the temporary buildings could be completed many churches, especially those whose congregations were considered disloyal, were confiscated and put to use as hospitals. Complaining was considered unpatriotic, even unchristian. The Henrys attended the same church as President Lincoln did, the New York Avenue Presbyterian Church, so they didn't have to worry about it being confiscated. The Henry girls were too young to be nurses under the strict rules laid down by Dorothea Dix so they had to be content to go with their mother to visit the wounded and take them books and home-cooked food. Mary was touched by the sight of liberated slaves getting off the ships that brought the wounded, looking around fearfully as if they longed for the security of their old Virginia home. Joseph Henry, who knew only what his secesh friends had told him about Negroes, expected them to die out as a race if left to themselves.

Evenings when Joseph wasn't visiting around with the members of his club, the family gathered under the gas chandelier with its opalescent glass shades at the round table in the parlor. Henry would recount to them the doings of his day, they would read aloud from their favorite poets, write letters, and play games. One evening when Mary's mother was writing to Mrs. John Bell of Tennessee, her father took the letter, added a postscript, and sealed up the envelope without letting Harriet read what he'd written. The more she protested the more he laughed. Another night they played a game with counters to great merriment. When Professor Welling of Columbia College came to protest a story he'd heard, the one about the mountain goat that had legs shorter on one side than the other, Henry thought it was funny and refused to write the papers complaining about this slur on the doctrine of First Causes.

One night there was an aurora, rare this far south. Remembering the more frequent auroras of the North, crackling blue and red and yellow like this across the sky, they stood silent on the grounds, watching. They forgot to worry about the rumored draft, and that Will might have to go in the Army.

At last it was agreed that in the fall Harriet and the girls could have a little vacation, a few weeks in the country away from malarial Washington. A farm near Sykesville, Maryland, was chosen as being quiet, out of the war's way, and with safe water and good food.

Sykesville, Maryland, five miles off the main road from Baltimore to Frederick, in September of 1862! Joseph Henry left his wife and daughters and hurried back to keep watch over the Smithsonian Institution, sure that they were all right. They had hardly gotten their little trunks unpacked when the mails stopped and the rumors began. The Army of Northern Virginia had invaded Maryland! Lee and Jackson were pillaging the countryside! Rebel pickets were within four miles of them! If there were any lingering secessionist sympathies in the Henry women's hearts they vanished.

Professor Henry, having heard the news in Washington,

came for them driving a wagon he had gotten for an exorbitant price in Baltimore. Hastily throwing their stuff in it, they set off for safety. Before they got to the turnpike they were stopped by two rebel pickets wearing homespun and mounted on suspiciously fresh, spirited horses. Horrified, acutely conscious of being part of the federal government, imagining themselves important prisoners, they locked their name in their throats and stared at their young, hard-faced captors. Even the familiar soft accent could not reassure them.

No, they did not know where any federal troops were. Not a one. No.

They were permitted to go on their way, the big, gray-haired man with the pretty little dark-haired wife beside him and three daughters perched undignifiedly on their trunks behind them.

Baltimore was as near bedlam as it had been during the riots of April 1861. Jackson was reported devouring all before him like the plague. Jeb Stuart's men were eight and ten deep all over Maryland. The trains North were jammed but Joseph Henry got the women on one of them and safely off to Philadelphia, then he returned to Washington.[22]

Union and Confederate armies finally met at Antietam (or Sharpsburg) on September 17, 1862. The Confederates won, but had to fall back to Virginia, leaving the bloodiest battlefield of the war.

Henry had to go to New York on business early in October, with Jeb Stuart still raiding in Maryland, the Emancipation Proclamation being eagerly discussed, and fever rampaging in Washington. He went to Philadelphia, got Harriet and the girls, and took them to the Alexanders' in Princeton. Then he and Harriet went on to New York. A letter came to Princeton from his secretary, saying that Will, who was at the Smithsonian during their absence, was very sick. Then

182

came a telegram, saying Will was much worse. Nell and Carrie were barely concerned but Mary, suddenly apprehensive, hurried to New York and then went back to Washington with her parents.

It was the hottest October in the history of the town. Helpless, doctor's care and medicine to no avail, they watched Will's suffering and saw the inexorable approach of the end of his brief life. In his delirium he thought he was still alone, and would take his medicine only from De Bust, the museum repairman. In the grip of typhoid he became so acutely nervous that he could stay in one place only about fifteen minutes. Then Henry Horan, the night watchman, and Hannah Patterson, the cook, would pick up his wasted frame and carry him to another bed, another big chair, and so on around the apartment. "Just this once more," he would beg, "and then I won't ask again." Nellie and Carrie were sent for, but before they could arrive he had burned and faded away before the anguished eyes of Joseph and Harriet and Mary and the close Smithsonian family. He died on October 17, 1862.

It was December 13 before Mary wrote in her diary again: *Father has been touchingly gentle since Will's death. He speaks of him quietly and cheerfully but we can see that it is telling on him.*

NOTES TO CHAPTER NINE

1. Trains are almost invariably so referred to at this time.
2. Soon to be replaced by the incorruptible Edwin M. Stanton.
3. Sir Edward Bulwer-Lytton's *Last Days of Pompeii* had been a best seller since 1834.
4. Mary Henry's diary for May 3, 1861.
5. Washington's bridges don't carry "the" in front of

them, if one wants the music as well as the words of the town. Only the now-vanished Aqueduct Bridge carried the article. So we have Long Bridge or Fourteenth Street Bridge and Chain Bridge today, plus the new ones, Key, Memorial, and Sousa.

6. None of Lowe's balloons was ever shot down and he had as many as three up at once during the siege of Richmond in 1862. The silk gas bags were not bulletproof and the rebels shot at them.

7. *Star*, July 11, 1861.

8. If Mary had a romantic attachment she concealed it very well. Her "dates" were to walk home from Sunday school with one of the professors or go for a carriage ride to see the war sights. After Bull Run she mentions having heard of the deaths of several friends, but no one is ever singled out.

9. These headlines from the *Star* are about a skirmish of troops on the nineteenth. The *Star* did not publish on Sundays. The handbills which were passed out were chaotic repetitions of Friday's headlines.

10. *Abraham Lincoln, the War Years*, by Sandburg. The night watchman's name is from the 1860 census and Mary Henry's diary.

11. Sentiments quoted by Coulson in *Joseph Henry, His Life and Works*, from an unidentified writing of L. E. Chittenden, Register of the Treasury during Lincoln's administration. They are borne out by Henry's surviving correspondence.

12. Mary Henry's diary.

13. The official naval reports on the progress of reducing the observations for the star catalog give the work as being either six or eleven years behind when Maury left. The farther one gets away from the hatred of the war years the more perspective one finds in the "records."

14. Newcomb had no way of knowing Maury wasn't telling the strict, exact truth.

15. *Reminiscences of an Astronomer*, by Newcomb. Apparently Professor Newcomb was also a believer in doing things the right way instead of the Navy way, because the Navy is still bragging about this old monstrosity.

16. *The Scientific American,* February 1, 1862. Such examples of ill-thought-out impetuosity and the failure of the Navy to build ironclads earlier provoked the editors to call them all "imbiciles" at this time. Any "mo-holers" want to join?

17. *Lincoln and the Tools of War,* by Bruce. Jefferson Davis was Secretary of War at this time.

18. *The Scientific American,* March 22, 1862. The elided phrase—*a massive wedge being driven below the step of the shaft on such occasions to raise it and thus cause it to bear up the turret.*—is not borne out by the many diagrams available of the workings of the *Monitor* and was apparently inserted to confuse the enemy, although that seems to have been a minor consideration of the times.

19. "In the 'Monitor' Turret," S. D. Greene, *Century* Magazine, March 1885.

20. From an article by Lowe in *Photographic History of the Civil War.* His work is also currently (1862) reported in *The Scientific American.*

21. The last time I was in the Peninsula this old house (they have a fancy name for it now, but it's there if you want to look for it) was open to the public for a fee. To those used to the Civil War pictures, when the roof was covered with the scaffolding of a Union signal station, it doesn't look quite right, but it is very beautiful. The furniture the Yankees broke up has been replaced with lovely old pieces bought from other houses of the same period in the neighborhood.

22. Mary Henry's diary.

was one of the officers Maury had reported to the Secretary of the Navy for failing to fill in the abstract logs that facilitated making wind and current charts.

Maury had a strong sense of his own importance as a world figure and felt that, since everyone else must realize it, too, it would be ludicrous for him to pretend to modesty. However justified, that attitude made it impossible to forget old hard feelings, and affairs went from bad to worse. Stephen Mallory was monumentally inept and Maury's superior attitude and bright ideas only antagonized him to the point where he eventually refused to put up with Maury any longer.

In April of 1861 Maury was appointed to Governor Letcher's advisory council and commissioned a commander in the Navy of the state of Virginia. In May Virginia ratified the Articles of Secession and Maury was soon made a commander in the Confederate States Navy, which consisted of captured lighthouse tenders, Coast Survey schooners, revenue cutters, and the wreckage of the Gosport Navy Yard at Norfolk. Put in charge of the Bureau of Coast, Harbor, and River Defense, Maury joined in helping fortify various areas such as Jamestown Island. But he had gotten one of his ideas, not original, but one that could be developed into something useful for the Confederacy, and it nagged at his thoughts day and night.

His family had been in Fredericksburg when he resigned and while he was in Richmond they stayed on with Cousin John Minor in his fine big house on Main Street. Maury felt that Washington would be the scene of the battles that were sure to come and consequently Fredericksburg might be too close to the action, so he tried to get them to move to Charlottesville. Mrs. Maury took to her bed with shock and dismay and refused to move any place. Mrs. Betty Maury and Nannie, "Curly," Corbin had to leave their homes so they came to stay and brought their kids. Dick, still in love with Susan Crutchfield, joined the 24th Virginia Volunteer In-

fantry Regiment. Dabney resigned his commission in the
United States Army and came back alone from Santa Fe
through the Indian country to take up a commission in the
Confederate army, and Davy Jones left V.M.I. and prepared
to join up, too.

For the next four years Richmond's seven hills were alive
as never before nor since. Volunteer troops in colorful and
quaint uniforms thronged the streets and courted the women
and fought in whisky dens and rattled their drums and fired
their guns and pulled their long bowie knives and tooted on
bugles and drove the good folks of Richmond half mad.
Richmond, a busy manufacturing town, was not so quiet and
easily distracted as Washington, but they were accustomed
to jogging along in their own little rut, nevertheless. At the
foot of the steep bluff where Gamble's Hill drops off into the
James the Tredegar Iron Works glowed redly all night and
the heavy drop of presses and banging of hammers never
stopped. On Shockoe the capital was thronged with office
seekers, contractors, inventors, politicians, members of the
First Families and riffraff and rabble. Chimborazo was the
scene of armed camps and the Kanawha Canal, and all
bridges over to Manchester were thronged with traffic to the
factories, camps, and farms across the James. The old fair-
grounds became Camp Lee. Between Cary Street and the
never-silent James, gurgling over the rapids that mark the
end of the tide water, were warehouses and factories filling
the air with the unforgettable, throat-searing smell of tobacco. Up and down the steep hills and out Franklin, Main,
Cary, Grace, Broad, Clay, went the soldiers and all the
scrambling busyness. The railroad cars came down Broad and
stopped at sheds in the heart of town, so all the troop de-
partures north to garrison Manassas Junction were public
and frequently emotional. The town was jammed not only
with troops, government officials, and contractors, but also

with refugees from Washington, northern and western Virginia, and points north. Even the Cary girls, from abandoned "Vauclose" near Fairfax, had to stay in a dreadful old building, the Clifton Hotel, and could receive their callers only by going outside and to another building. They had put "Maryland, My Maryland" to music, and it was a favorite song with the soldiers,[1] along with "Lorena," "Dixie," and "The Girl I Left Behind Me."

Letters written by Maury during this period contain utterances that can only be explained as the madness of war-born hatred. It rankled with him that his resignation had been refused by the Secretary of the Navy and that instead he had been dismissed from the service, despite his high-handed letter saying he knew of no reason why he had to explain his resignation. When accused in the northern press of stealing charts and having the buoys removed from Kettle Bottom Shoals he wrote angrily that he had touched them not, and that he had gone with a state which had left a tyrannical government for reasons far more just than the New England states had had to withdraw from the status of British colonies. He suggested as a cure for "excessive democracy" that votes be apportioned by wealth, each person acquiring voting rights like shareholders in a stock company.[2] And on July 19, 1861, with the Battle of First Manassas (Bull Run) not yet fought, he wrote from Richmond to an unnamed friend (probably his cousin Frank Minor in Charlottesville) that the enemy had freed their slaves, burned their property, confiscated their possessions, and were enslaving them and that anything, even poisoned food, would be a legitimate weapon against them.[3]

The humanitarian-of-the-seas had turned to inventing infernal machines, so possibly he was trying to find a justification for his actions.

In his cousin Robert Maury's house at 1105 East Clay

Street, Maury was hooking up batteries and wires and explosives in an attempt to make a practical underwater mine, which others called torpedoes. Bushnell had made the first mines in America, Fulton had worked on them, and twenty years ago young Sam Colt had been making such successful mines that one he exploded under a raft blew the contents of a pond all over the suddenly-enraged spectators of his Independence Day fireworks. Maury's letters indicate that he was ordering carboys of nitric acid (for batteries), quicksilver, sulphur, and so on. Planning eventually to develop a mine that could be fired from the shore by batteries sending a current through wire, he was working now on a type of contact mine. Two barrels coated inside with tar to make them waterproof contained black powder, and were tied together by a rope. When floated down-current, anything catching or pulling on the rope triggered detonators which set off the powder. They were sometimes temperamental in operation and occasionally it seemed that everything that could go wrong with them did so.

Enraged by Secretary of the Navy Mallory's jeers, Maury challenged him to watch a demonstration in the James off Rocketts. He vindicated himself and shut Mallory up by having a successful show: the mine went off and blew water and expiring fish all over everything. But a week later, when with muffled oars and in the dead of night he and a crew of volunteers rowed out to where the *Minnesota* lay at anchor off Fortress Monroe, the rope failed to trip the detonators, and the *Minnesota* survived to be run aground by the *Virginia* and rescued by the *Monitor* on a memorable weekend in March of the following year. The mines were found floating in Hampton Roads several days later and sent to Washington for analysis, after which the federal navy got orders to put out small boats and nets to protect their ships. All Maury and his crew of volunteers could do was glumly row back to

Sewall's Point and start again. It had taken one kind of courage for a little man with a game leg, past fifty-five, to lead such an expedition; it took another kind to go on with the experiments in the face of such a failure.

On June 19, 1861, he got on the cars and went up to Fredericksburg for the weekend, just as Dabney arrived from the West. All day Sunday they heard the rumble of artillery in the distance like thunder and, finally, to their great relief, word came that the day had been won at Manassas. It was what everyone had expected. Yankees were shopkeepers; they couldn't fight. And leaders? How proud they were knowing that three Confederate generals had died at Manassas, and Thomas J. Jackson had won the name "Stonewall." The Yankee leaders, it was said, had led the panic flight.

Maury made a proposal that the Confederate government sue for peace as soon as the hubbub in Richmond died down. Craftily he explained that he didn't really want peace, and knew such a proposition was futile. But an enormous number of northerners hated the war, he thought, and news that the South wanted peace would cause an immense rift in the Yankee war effort. He interested quite a few people in the idea, but nothing came of it.

All of his property outside of the Confederacy he had sold by his agent and former teacher, William Hasbrouck of Newburgh, New York, and the money invested in Confederate bonds. The property of some rebels in the North was being confiscated; Robert E. Lee had even lost his home in Virginia, since it was so close to Washington, and Maury, who knew Lee well, was exercising his French caution. Rutson Maury kept on acting as his banker, friend and critic.

All summer long he kept up his work on the mines. In one of his letters he says he "damaged" two Yankee steamers, a claim nowhere substantiated by federal records. However, we

192

must remember, the Yankees were pretty nervous on the subject of mines and if they could blame damage by them on something else, such as uncharted shoals, they would. They had green crews and officers, too, in their suddenly expanded navy and they didn't want any panics or mutinies.

In the fall Maury began to write for the newspapers again on naval matters, using the name "Ben Bow." Down at the Gosport Navy Yard his former lieutenant, John Brooke, inventor of the depth-sounding apparatus of which Maury approved so highly, was superintending the rebuilding of the partly-burned and sunk steam frigate *Merrimac*. Maury, who had been on the advisory council that had recommended the job, now turned his thinking in the direction of substitutes for shot proofs. Speed, or a tiny target, there was your answer. He began to advocate with characteristic sharp insistency that gunboats be built in quantity to protect the harbors, rivers, and coast line entrusted to his care. It was not too practicable a proposal, in the circumstances then existing. Steam engines were expensive and difficult to procure; the South just did not have them to install in small boats. As for guns, besides being expensive and scarce there were other problems. A big gun would put a gunboat completely awash, as witness the hundreds of American gunboats built after the Tripolitan War—they rocked so violently after each shot that they could be fired only every half-hour.[4] A small gun had only a nuisance value.

But Maury's prestige with the public had shot up enormously, so that Mallory and others began to give in to him a little. Came the British consulate messenger from Washington under a flag of truce with a formal letter for Maury from the Grand Duke Constantine, Grand Admiral of Russia, offering him and his family a home and an income in peaceful, backward Russia. Another letter, from Baron Stoeckle, the Russian ambassador, offered his services in making all the necessary arrangements. It made quite a stir, and Maury hurried to Fredericksburg to read the contents of the big, stiff-folded pages to his family.[5] How they all glowed at the praises, and the sense of being appreciated and rewarded for work well done, but they all realized that it was an honor impossible of acceptance. Maury had cast his lot with the Confederacy for better or for worse, and there was no sacrifice he would not make to help the cause. He was a great man and he would be great on behalf of his native soil and it amused him not at all.

The government ordered one hundred of his gunboats to be built: 112 feet long, 21 feet wide, powered by steam, with a 9-inch rifled Parrot gun forward and a little bulldog popgun aft. They started building them at Fredericksburg and at Norfolk, but the serious shortage of war material in the South slowed down their construction to a frustrating series of fits and starts. The Tredegar Iron Works—*the* ironworks of the South, to all intents and purposes—was now engaged in arming an army and the new-raised hulk of the *Merrimac,* both of which took considerable doing. Fittings for a hundred gunboats somehow got shoved to the end of the line. The steam engines proved unattainable. The work dragged on, into a mortifying doldrums.

Dabney, now married to Rose Mason, had set up a home for her and his mother, but remained as close as ever to his foster family. When he was commissioned a brigadier general in the Confederate army they were all proud and happy for him, and his overjoyed young cousin John Herndon Maury (otherwise "Davy Jones"), formerly a private, was made his aide-de-camp with the rank of lieutenant. Dabney admits in his charming *Recollections of a Virginian* that he had asked for Johnny in order to keep an eye on him, because he was something of an exotic and army life was unduly rough on him. Johnny was a lovable youngster with a quaint lisp,

194

handsome, gentle, seemingly incapable of taking any kind of care of himself; he would not show any emotion no matter how badly he was hurt. That he would be "numbered with the slain," as the currently popular song put it,[6] seemed a dreadful foreboding. Dabney took his nineteen-year-old cousin west with him to help manage the troops—among them a regiment of tall Texans armed with repeating rifles, laughing at their astonished faces at the sight of himself, their general, blond, almost effeminately good-looking, not quite five feet three inches tall and, as it turned out, so strict and yet so daring that they became extremely proud of their "Little Dab."

Maury above all things loved his home, his family. He could not bear to be alone in the house, hearing his footsteps echo emptily through the silent rooms, no voice to answer his, no "presence" felt about him. But his family was never to be together again. He knew that Dabney would watch over Davy Jones as if he were his own son, but Dick was another matter. There was no doing anything with his eldest son, and never had been. Dick admitted this in his letters, saying in one that all his father had to do was tell him to do something for him to decide to do the opposite, even if he knew it would hurt him. He made no attempt to explain it, only tried to tell his father that he really did take his admonitions to heart, even if he didn't act on them.

At this time Dick, now a major, was trying to get leave from his regiment to get married. No leave was forthcoming. His father wrote a letter to Major General Van Dorn (this was before he was sent to the West) demanding that his son be given a leave, and this had done Dick no good with his colonel, Jubal Early.[7] But Dick was never content to let anyone else get him in trouble when he was so good at it himself, and what with his loud complaints, persistent requests, and unsoldierlike attitude, on top of his father's tactless letter, he got himself held for court-martial. Fortunately the exigencies of war didn't allow the matter to become serious.

In this winter of inactivity there was some excitement when the *San Jacinto* stopped the British steamer *Trent* and took off the Confederate commissioners, Mason and Slidell, to the early indignation and then great joy of the South. That imbecile Charles Wilkes had at last really overstepped himself! This might do the South some good, since now England could plainly see what a bunch of highhanded tyrants the South had seceded from. Mason and Slidell had safely run that cursed Yankee blockade and now it seemed they might force the issue for the South: recognition or a possible lifting of the blockade, if not actual war between the Union and England. But the English warehouses were full of cotton and the good queen's husband, dying, made one last gift to the people who had so spitefully used him, and insured that at least the *Trent* affair would not mean war. Both commissioners proceeded on to England, "happily" turned loose by the Yankees and put on a British warship, Mason going to England and Slidell to France, and neither to any purpose.

Early in 1862 work was halted on Maury's gunboats. None of them was ever put into commission.

In February Richmond had itself a handsome, young, dead hero: Jennings Wise, son of the former governor and captain of the Richmond Blues. Sent with his regiment to garrison Roanoke Island, he was mortally wounded and his outnumbered troops had to surrender. As he lay dying he told his captors that they would have to exterminate the people of the South, because they could never be conquered. His body was returned to the sorrowing town and lay in state in St. James Church under the flag for which he had died. On the coffin were his cloak and his sword, and evergreen branches cut by the young people of the town. Crowds stood weeping along the funeral route as the procession of town dignitaries followed his coffin.

Things were going badly in the West. Grant at Fort Donelson acquired his "Unconditional Surrender" nickname and Kentucky and west Tennessee were cut off from the rest of the South. The blockade was getting tighter and tighter. Everyone knew that the South would win eventually, of course, but it looked as if the heart-crushing struggle would go on and on and on.

Around Hampton Roads on the afternoon of March 8, 1862, everyone rushed to the gravelly beaches and turfy banks to watch the sea battle that they could not hear. A strong wind was blowing out of the west so that to the observers on the shore [8] it was like seeing the picture of a battle, the clouds of smoke spiraling up, the pinky-bright flashes of the big guns, the great ships sinking or going aground, the flames leaping up from the *Congress*, the pathetic flag of the *Cumberland* still flying a few feet above the water in which the ship had gone down, that great ironclad the *Virginia* with its rifled guns commanding all before it, and all around the flare and flash of the shore batteries, everything in strange, complete silence.

About four o'clock the wind fell, and the noise of the battle burst thunderously over the onlookers on the strand. But it had been a sight so eerie that no one would ever forget it: the triumphant *Virginia's* stilly battle with the Union fleet.

All night the fires and explosions on board the *Congress* lit the wide expanse of water under a pale new moon.[9] The *Virginia* would be back at dawn (minus her wounded captain, Franklin Buchanan, formerly of Washington's Navy Yard) to finish off these Yankees, and the crowd increased all night. Shortly before eight the *Virginia* with her escorts sallied forth to cheers. And from behind the grounded *Minnesota*

197

came a tiny boat at first believed to be a tug. A strange little craft, like a tin can on a shingle, that in utter madness accosted the *Virginia* and bounced a shot off her impenetrable sides. The *Virginia* replied in kind, but instead of disintegrating, the little craft shed the shot, smartly rotated its turret, and slammed two more shells at the *Virginia*. This kept up for four hours, the two ships at times so close they were grinding against each other, until at noon the *Monitor* sheered off, Captain Worden being blinded by a hit on the viewing slit of the pilothouse from which he was commanding the movements of the ship. The *Virginia*, seeing the *Monitor* apparently abandoning the fight, limped off to have trouble in her engines cared for. So ended the first battle of ironclads.

On the fifteenth Maury was writing to one of the French naval brass, a former correspondent on wind and current matters, a letter of twenty-seven large pages, boasting about the invincibility of the *Virginia* and describing how she was made.[10] The inventor of submarine mines, who had at least *tried* to kill men while they slept (a notion he admitted to being squeamish about), cursed Union Admiral Charles Davis for blockading Charleston harbor by sinking stone boats across the entrance, and so destroying "the haven of the storms." And this from one who had enjoyed the town's hospitality! A "gentleman Turk," Maury called Davis, and blamed him for burning the *Merrimac*, which belonged to the South as much as to the North, their taxes having helped pay for it. Much as he wanted to discredit Davis, who was head of the Bureau of Navigation (and one of Joseph Henry's closest friends), the letter was obviously an attempt to sell the Confederacy as being unconquerable, particularly by those Yankee beasts. He compared secession with the French Revolution, a favorite gambit of the Confederates. Here and there a spirit of desperation seemed to show through the grand phrases.

After the battle of the ironclads there was a great storm in Chesapeake Bay and the frantically-laid cable from Cape Charles to Fortress Monroe was torn loose (in many places the water in Hampton Roads is less than fifteen feet deep) and cast up on the Confederate-held shore. Here was ten miles of insulated copper wire, much of it in usable condition, for Maury to use on his mines. He turned his considerable powers to bear upon the problem. In May of 1862, with the Peninsula, Hampton Roads, even the James up to where Fort Darling stood on Drewry's Bluff, literally thick with Yankees, he set out on another mine-laying expedition. He made his will before he left.[11]

Assisted by Lieutenant Hunter Davidson in the first mine layer, the little tug *Teaser*, Maury put out fifteen real mines in the James River below Chaffin's Bluff. They were of boiler plate made some by Tredegar and some by Talbot and Son, and contained from 70 to 160 pounds of powder, each encased in a watertight wooden cask capable of floating it. They were held below the surface of the water by anchors and all tied together by long ropes. They could be fired by an operator from the shore, singly and at will. He listed among those who helped him one Lieutenant William L. Maury and a Dr. Moore who was president of the Telegraph Company. Then he turned the whole thing over to Hunter Davidson to manage.[12]

Maury himself never exploded a fatal mine. But these mines which he placed in the James at this time were to be successfully fired later on in the war, after months, almost years, of submersion. He sent instructions to the Confederate forces on the Mississippi on how to make these mines, and others picked up his work and improvised on it. During the Peninsular campaign, Yankee soldiers were reputedly killed by land mines outside Williamsburg.[13]

The Yankee observation balloons hung in the spring sky

day after day. The Confederate forces kept slowly falling back, stalling, delaying, thankful for the rains that mudholed the roads and mired the heavy Yankee wagon trains with their rich loads of supplies, trying to give Johnston time to get Richmond's defenses ready. They didn't know McClellan had been licked (in his heart) even before he started, by an order depriving him of McDowell's 40,000 men, held to defend Washington.

On May 11, 1862, the Confederates abandoned the Gosport Navy Yard and burned it rather more completely than Hiram Paulding had on the hasty night a year before when he had tried to undo the treachery there. And Josiah Tatnall, old "blood is thicker than water" Tatnall, now commanding the *Virginia,* ordered it destroyed. She drew more than twenty feet of water and the Confederate navy was pulling back up the James. Maury sat on the court-martial that afterward exonerated Tatnall of all blame for the loss of the *Virginia.* Incidentally, after joining in the futile assault on Drewry's Bluff the *Monitor* was lost during a storm at sea while under tow by the side-wheeler *Rhode Island,* bound for an assault on Charleston, December 29, 1862.[14]

At Seven Pines (Fair Oaks), on the last of May 1862, Joseph E. Johnston was wounded and Robert E. Lee, formerly Jefferson Davis's advisor on military matters, took charge of the army. After some minor brushes the two armies fought again at Mechanicsville (Beaver Dam), then at Cold Harbor (Gaines's Mill), then at Savage Station, then at White Oak Swamp, and at last at Malvern Hill. Taken together this was the Seven Days' Battle, from June 26 to July 2, 1862, when McClellan finally succeeded in getting a new base at Harrison's Landing. The Union forces had won almost every engagement; but they could not take Richmond.

The people of Richmond didn't know that, however. From late May, when the battle of Seven Pines was fought beside

200

the Chickahominy [15] until McClellan successfully withdrew
to Harrison's Landing, there was the rumble of artillery
and the clatter of alarums and excursions in Richmond without letup. When there weren't torrents of rain, and everything
awash, it was hot and dusty and humid. Never was there such
a season for growing things, and the lilacs and magnolias
and dogwood and Judas tree and crape myrtle ran to such
splendor that even the sick hearts were forced to take notice.
There was hardly a family in Richmond who didn't have someone out there in the forefront of battle. Every building that
could be used was requisitioned as a hospital, and the servants were sent out to look for their masters and help bring
in the wounded. Dignified old butlers carried trays of food,
creamed things for invalids, and the best old wines, to the
wounded and suffering. There were thousands of them, but
little medicine or chloroform. Young women were pressed
into duty as nurses. The dust-clouded streets were thronged
with carriages and wagons carrying the wounded in and
supplies out. Householders never knew when a makeshift con-
veyance would stop at their door and they would run out to
find their heart's dearest covered with dirt, blood, flies, lying
there dead or dying. Sometimes neighbors ran away down the
streets, holding up their hoopskirts, unable to bear it. The
sound of the fighting never seemed to stop.

On May 31, 1862, in the early evening a horseman pulled
up at Robert Maury's house and called to Mat that his son
was lying wounded near Seven Pines and wanted him. Maury
hastily got a horse and buggy and set out down the road
toward Fair Oaks. The battle was still going on and the road
and roadside were littered with the wounded and dying. After
an agonizing search, going forward each step with the dread
thought that he had missed his son dying behind some bush,
the night coming on, Maury at last found him about five miles
from town, sitting on a grassy bank whistling, his right arm

broken by a "minnie" ball. Maury thankfully hustled him into the buggy, home, and to bed.

Within a week Dick was back in camp, and soon succeeded in getting married to his Susan, who had to come through the Union lines in most romantic fashion. Simpering, affected, she drove Dick's family to openly unfriendly remarks; she retaliated by labeling his sisters as too "satirical" for her.

Maury, his torpedo mission accomplished, went to see Secretary of the Navy Stephen Mallory to ask what he could do for the Confederacy now. Mallory, no doubt enjoying himself, told Maury he could be of great service doing nothing.

Things got so serious in Richmond that Maury sent his letter books to Frank Minor in Charlottesville for safekeeping, thus confirming that part of the family's fears for their capital.

In the depths of depression, his family broken up, his talents unwanted, his country facing extinction, Maury became quite morose. Thoughts of suicide came. *I feel quite indifferent to life. I would cultivate this fashion were it not cowardly, mean, and selfish*, he wrote to Frank Minor in June of 1862. He had no hopes for the holding of Richmond, by anything short of an act of God.

By mid-July, with McClellan gone and Richmond surprisingly still intact, Maury had cheered up. He wrote to William Hasbrouck in Newburgh, New York, that he had succeeded in locating Hasbrouck's son, who had been listed as missing during the Peninsular campaign, and that he was a prisoner of war in a camp near Saulsbury, North Carolina. After promising to see that he was well treated, Maury burst forth with a great surge of enthusiasm for his Confederacy and for his own sons in the fighting, adding, *Glorious cause. Great boys*.

Two weeks later he had to write General McClellan a begging letter for the persons of his children, Fredericks-

burg having been peacefully occupied by McDowell's forces
during the Peninsular campaign while Big Nannie was in
Richmond visiting him. General Lee even ordered J. E. B.
Stuart to send a messenger to the lines to inquire for them.
Then, suddenly, the Army of Northern Virginia had trounced
a Union army under General Pope, again at Manassas late
in August 1862, and Fredericksburg was safe.

The war was being lost in the West, where "Little Dab"
and his young aide Davy Jones were fighting. And on the
seacoast, where the blockade was strangling the South bit
by bit, no matter how the new-launched *Alabama* and her
sister ships tried to scour the Yankee merchant shipping
from the seas in an effort to draw the Union navy away.

Maury's country was at war and all things were grist to
his mill. His hatred of the Union was rich, widespread, and
capable of growing. In the case of the torpedoes he had
worried because by making them he had destroyed his reputation for doing good. Not about his doing good, but about his
reputation along that line.[16] This was the blind thinking of
hatred, and it was but a step to further vindictiveness. Proud
of his ability as a writer, he kept up a steady stream of abuse
of the North to foreign scientists and government notables.
After all, not only the Grand Admiral of Russia but Napoleon
III had asked him to give up the South and make his home
abroad, with peace and honors. On August 4, 1862, he wrote
Admiral Fitzroy in London twenty-two pages: *The Yankees
are a nation of shop keepers, you know. . . . The impression exists that Mr. Seward has intimidated both England
and France. . . . The Northern people are already tired of
this war. . . . The old government of the United States
had become utterly corrupt.* He began to dwell on his vast
fame abroad. He was little appreciated in the South because
his talents had gone to make the Yankee shipowners rich, and
had made the sea safe for a not particularly seagoing nation.

Stephen Mallory now had an idea that would solve the Maury problem—get the man out of the country! Send him to England as one of the Confederate naval commissioners who were getting ships such as the *Alabama* to sea. Maury knew that if he went it would overjoy his enemies in the Confederate government. On the other hand, he had many friends in England. He had this great reputation. He was wasted in Richmond through no fault of his own, the little jealous men holding him down and keeping him in the background, and he owed it to his country to make every sacrifice. He should go to England. He had made those Yankee sea captains rich; now he would sweep their ships off the sea. He knew more about the sea than any man alive. He would remind them of it; he would rub their noses in it.

He couldn't abandon his family, neither could he take them along. He and Big Nannie had a long conference. Two of her brothers, John and Brodie, were in Fredericksburg and could help look after her and the girls. Matthew Fontaine Maury, Junior, Matsy to the family and Brave to his pa, he would take with him. There was nothing he could do to help Dick, and Davy Jones was far away in the West with Dabney, who had just missed Shiloh, fought nobly at Corinth, and was now just before Vicksburg. Of all his children, Davy Jones was his favorite.

Having done the thinking, now they had to do the doing and be going. Matsy had a new pair of winter pants, made from a pair of his pa's old ones by that excellent tailor, Sister Eliza, and for a winter coat an old one of Dave's. It was not that the Maurys were poor: it was the blockade. Along with his instructions from the Confederate government was another commission, clothes and shoes and medicine for his family.

Fraser and Trenholm was one of the Confederate blockade-running companies and Trenholm one of the richest men in the South. It was to him in Charleston that Maury and Matsy went in late September 1862 to get through the blockade and safely away to England. Trenholm was all attention, Maury's *Sailing Directions* hardly being out of his captain's hands, and even provided them with a young midshipman, James Morris Morgan, who, in his old age, wrote one of the most quoted books about the Confederate navy. They made their first attempt to get out of Charleston Harbor on September 24, 1862. It was the middle of October before they made it. The *Herald*, which Maury called the *Hero* in the letters he wrote home to "Dear Friend" (obviously his wife), was one of the famous blockade-running ships. Mr. Morgan gets the ship safely to St. George, Bermuda, after sundry exciting adventures in his *Recollections of a Rebel Reefer*, which at least makes entertaining reading. Maury only comments to his wife on the behavior of their brave son, who was a little seasick but not much, and withstood the rough and dangerous trip under the noses of the Yankee navy excellently. He doesn't mention Morgan at all, as a matter of fact. In St. George he found the British exceedingly polite and was told that the hated Captain Wilkes and his fast steamer had just left. He sent a parcel of shoes and sundries home, with the promise of more from England, and when the mail steamer arrived they were off for Halifax. They were seasick for almost a week, and landed in snow and miserable cold. Matsy wrote his mother excellent letters, if brief, well spelled considering his age, his penmanship large, round, and legible. An organ grinder played "Dixie" under their hotel window all day, and his father bought him new warm clothes. There were parties and much evidence of his father's importance, and a meeting with Colonel LeMat, the French sidearm inventor. Matsy thought the whole thing a lark.

At last the Cunard steamer *Arabia* arrived from Boston, bound for Liverpool, and to the plainly-spoken outrage of the Yankee passengers, crippled little Commander M. F. Maury, C.S.N., and his party set out on the last leg of their voyage to England, where they were to spend the rest of the war.[17]

NOTES TO CHAPTER TEN

1. "A Virginia Girl in the First Year of the War," by C. C. Harrison, *Century Magazine*, August 1885.

2. To Rutson Maury, March 29, 1861.

3. Possibly Maury put the wrong year on the letter, which we have all done at one time or another. If not—well, he hadn't seen anything yet! Only a year before he had written Rutson that he preferred Lincoln for president, then Bell.

4. *Compact History of the U. S. Navy*, by Pratt.

5. Preserved with the other Maury papers at the Library of Congress.

6. But one cheerful line from a popular ballad of the times, "Just before the Battle, Mother."

7. This was before Early's promotion, of course.

8. "Watching the Merrimac," by R. E. Colston, *Century Magazine*, March 1885.

9. In different versions of the battle different things happen.

10. The French had a partly ironclad ship, *La Gloire*, and the British had one, the *Warrior*. Both were only armored amidships, according to *The Scientific American*.

11. May 4, 1862. He left everything to his wife with the exception of the medals he'd gotten for his oceanographic discoveries from foreign governments, which were distributed among his children.

12. *A Brief Sketch of the Work of Matthew Fontaine Maury During the War 1861–65*, by R. L. Maury, the "impossible Dick" of this book, who blithely tells how he accom-

panied his father on some of his mine-laying ventures, which took place when his letters show he was with his regiment.

13. "Recollections of a Private: Up the Peninsula with McClellan," W. L. Goss, *Century Magazine*, March 1885. I say "reputedly" because I don't find any official mention of it, and Goss was one of those who saw kilts on the Cameron Highlanders at Bull Run. But, on the other hand, we'll see Maury making land mines later, in England.

14. An excellent account of this appears in "The Loss of the Monitor, by a Survivor," by Francis Butts, one of the Rhode Island Historical Society pamphlets, reprinted in the *Century Magazine*, December 1885.

15. All this area in the Peninsula is well worth seeing today. It has changed but little, the low bridges but barely over river and swamp, the farms, the old houses, the forests, the crossroad villages, the breastworks through the woods still visible (those in the fields, of course, are gone).

16. Letter to Frank Minor, November 5, 1861.

17. Except young Morgan. He went on to so many adventures ashore and afloat that one can hardly keep up with them.

CHAPTER ELEVEN

Henry and the War in Washington (Part Two)

IT WAS A SAD Christmas for the Henrys, their first without Will, everyone under the strain of forced cheerfulness and a determination not to break down and show how they really felt. In the evening Joseph read "The Lady of the Lake" aloud from the book of Scott's poems which had been his Christmas present to Carrie, and much as Mary enjoyed it, she found herself remembering a Christmas several years before, the first when Will had his own money, and gave their mother thirty or forty dollars to buy presents for all of them.[1] Two days later "the Club" met at their apartment, the close friends of her father: Bache; Admiral Davis, who looked like an Elizabethan seadog; General Montgomery Meigs, formerly in charge of construction of the Capitol and now Quartermaster General; Captain Gilliss; Joseph Saxton the inventor and instrument maker; William B. Taylor, a local scientist; Arnold Guyot, the meteorologist; and others, both permanent members and visitors, who had an informal meeting weekly at each others' homes just to "chin." All said how much they missed Will and agreed that the prospects for peace looked very dim. News of the loss of the *Monitor* didn't cheer them up any.

It was a sad Christmas for all of the North, that of 1862. Washington was like a great hospital, with a rumored 13,000 men lying there sick, wounded, dying. On December 13 the shocking battle of Fredericksburg had been fought, when Union troops had died like flies assaulting the strongly fortified hilltop positions of the Rebels across the Rappahannock, and back they had come by the trainload, the shipload. A friend of the Henrys, named McIntyre, had gone to Fredericksburg to get his brother who was sick there, but had to come back without him because of the battle. His ride back to Washington in a trainload of wounded was too harrowing to bear; he had climbed up on the roof and sat on a coffin, at least no longer able to see the dreadful sights, even if he still had to listen to the groans and outcries of the suffering men.

The Armory Square hospital had been built next to the Smithsonian on the east, a clump of neat little sheds, curtained, painted white, with paths raised above the mud. The wounded were in large wards, the heads of their narrow white cots along the wall, stoves and water coolers down the middle of the room, flowers on the bedside tables, pious mottoes on the walls, and one of Miss Dorothea Dix's nurses on duty.[2] Mary Felton, daughter of Professor Felton of the Smithsonian staff, young and attractive, was one of the nurses here. Mary Henry and her mother and sisters were frequent callers. One day Miss Dix, who was in charge of all the Union nurses, came to visit Professor Henry and stayed for dinner. She reacted to Nurse Mary Felton with shocked disbelief. She had given strict orders that only middle-aged women, plain to the point of homeliness, of unblemished reputation and strict Protestants, were to be hired. The warm recommendation of the Henrys and her patients did no good. Nurse Felton had to go. Henry quietly went on supplying disinfectants to what Miss Dix regarded as her hospitals.

Alexander Dallas Bache was a member of the Sanitary Commission, which directed the hospitals and relief work, and frequently discussed with Henry the problems they had with all their medical staff. Directors who were political hacks, surgeons who operated while they were drunk, nurses who tried to run everything, doctors who (after one run-in with Miss Dix) would allow only Sisters of Charity in their hospitals, the lack of asepsis, and the alarming mortality rate. Still, for something that had been concocted to cover occasions as they came up, the Sanitary Commission worked surprisingly well. Miss Dix, still extremely attractive though no longer young, was using her own fortune to further the good work, maintaining her own fleet of ambulances, renting two large adjoining houses which she used as offices in Washington, traveling to the Union hospitals in every area to make sure they were run correctly. The government was forced by the volume of public opinion to outdo her. Some of her nurses apparently worked themselves to death, and many died of fevers and other contagions caught in the wards. The name of "Mother" Bickerstaff, one of the hospital matrons, became a watchword in the language of the day; not even generals were immune to her demands on behalf of "her boys," and mere surgeons fled before her.[3]

Sanitary Fairs were all the rage in the large towns of the North and thousands of dollars were taken in to support the work of the Sanitary Commission, which also ran little canteens at the camps, helped disabled soldiers get pensions, and did the work of the Red Cross and other services of today. In Washington, however, the Sanitary Fairs, even the most elaborate, were dismal failures. The Henrys went to an ornate one, with tents on the lawn and all the elite there, which took in only three hundred dollars. "Too many secesh in town," everyone said.

Henry knew that Mrs. Lincoln had turned to spiritualism after the death of her Willie, and that one of the mediums, named Colchester, was remarkably clever at producing strange sounds at will. The Fox sisters had launched American spiritualism in 1848 in Rochester, New York. Henry knew that the Fox girls, who always carried on their meetings in the dark, were supposed to be able to pop the joints of their fingers loudly and so managed to produce the messages ("One for yes and two for no") which they claimed came from beyond the veil. But, Lincoln told Henry worriedly, Colchester did his spiritrapping in broad daylight and the sounds seemed to come from all parts of the room. Concerned for Mrs. Lincoln, the President asked Henry if he would give Colchester an interview and see if he could determine what produced the strange cracking sounds.

Spiritualism was something that Joseph Henry abhorred. When his friends told him of their experiences he criticized them forthrightly. One, a judge of the usual brand of rectitude, told of having seen a medium float out of a window, waft around outside like a feather, and fly back into the room again.

"Judge," Professor Henry said heatedly, "you never saw that, and if you think you did, you are in a dangerous mental condition. If you do not give this delusion up you will be in the insane asylum before you know it. As a loving friend I beseech you to take warning of what I say, and to reflect that what you think you saw is a mental delusion which requires the most careful treatment." [4]

But Colchester was another breed of cat. With an attitude of insolent superiority he condescended to make his noises for

212

the skeptical scientist—and proceeded to stump Henry completely.

"I do not know how you make the sounds, but this I perceive very clearly: they do not come from the room but from your person," the professor said at last.[5] The medium departed laughing.

However, it was only a short time before Henry found out quite by accident what caused the sounds. While making one of his frequent train trips he happened to sit beside a young man who engaged him in pleasant conversation. Henry introduced himself to the young man, who turned out to be a manufacturer of telegraph instruments.

"And do you know, Professor," he went on, "I also make them for spiritualists."

Henry gasped in surprise.

"Well, not real ones, of course. But a device that fits around the bicep, which, when the so-called medium expands the muscle, makes a sharp click like the telegraph key. The medium is loaded with apparatus but it's worth it to make such an impression on the unwary. Have you heard of that Colchester fellow? He uses my equipment." [6]

It was a great relief to Lincoln to learn that it was just a trick. He may have been on the verge of doubting his own beliefs, so hard pressed was he by other, weightier concerns.

On January 1, 1863, the Emancipation Proclamation [7] had shaken up the folks, black and white, and a little more than a month later Mary Henry wrote in her diary that there was great indignation over the law providing for the arming of 15,000 Negroes. She expected Maryland and West Virginia to leave the Union, but they didn't. She also expected Army officers to resign rather than lead Negro troops, but if any did their resignations were refused. The abject degradation of the Negro by slavery, by the lack of education, by the great force of an unenlightened public opinion, shows in the idea of the Negro as a sort of happy, irresponsible clown which was held then.[8] How there could be found white people to cry it down and give the Negro a chance is a wonder. In Washington the 3,000 slaves reported by the 1860 census had been liberated in 1862, their owners being paid three hundred dollars each for them. Now all the slaves in areas in armed rebellion against the federal government (that is, those over which it had no actual jurisdiction) were declared free. This was a source of joy to the abolitionists, but there were many soldiers who didn't feel like risking their lives in a war fought just to free "niggers," and they retaliated by busting every "nigger" they saw right in the eye. Even convalescents got up and popped the colored men who worked as orderlies in the hospitals. The town toughs, who were fighting men in their own estimation, were ready and eager to beat up Negroes and took to "laying" for them. The thousands of escaped Negroes who had congregated in Washington walked very quietly in their free town. They preferred to keep to themselves but soon overflowed their camps. The Negro regiments performed wonders for being made up of people with no background of tradition; every good thing they did was despite what was expected of them.

In all this turmoil of wounded in hospitals, free Negroes in Freedmen's Village, soldiers in training, and somehow all tossing rocks, Washington was as ready to explode as any "torpedo." Only the heroic efforts of the better citizens averted a race riot, which would have negated all the good the Emancipation Proclamation had done abroad.

Then something happened that was excruciatingly funny to the South, although the North got the last laugh. To the fretful tempers in Washington, it said: Get your minds off the colored problem, there's a war on. Out of no place, in the black of night, March 9, 1863, came John Singleton Mosby and his Partisan Rangers, who were considered guerrillas and liable to hanging if caught (few were either caught or hanged). They came to Fairfax Court House, that strongly-garrisoned Union army post about fifteen miles from Washington, and with blood-chilling screeches, whoops of the Rebel yell and helpless giggles, snatched Union General Stoughton away in his nightshirt and a great clatter of hoof-beats. One could laugh: not a soul was hurt. But the kidnaping of Stoughton brought his inefficiency (the man was a pompous loudmouth much disliked in Union army circles) into the limelight and after being ransomed from Richmond he was sent home in retirement and a worth-while officer was put in his place, one who saw that the approaches to Washington were guarded a little more alertly.

The battle named after Chancellorsville was on its way, and few smiles for anyone.

A permanent commission of three members—Admiral Davis, Professor Bache, and Joseph Henry—was formed to investigate for the government the scientific problems which had to do with the war. Henry had just been appointed a Commissioner of the Mint,[9] adding to his burden of travel, and was often off to Philadelphia where Joseph Saxton was working on minutely accurate scales to use in the annual assays. The permanent commission went to New York to the Navy Yard to work on the problem of installing compasses on iron ships. They came up with a jury-rigged affair, surrounded by magnets, which had to do until the British scientist William Thompson perfected one. This commission, so "permanent" that it lasted not quite a month before being made a committee of the ill-received National Academy of Sciences,[10] was designed primarily to get crackpots off the necks of cabinet members and the President. Besides this, the Smithsonian itself was, as usual, flooded with new ideas and Henry had to listen patiently to earnest inventors of torpedo balloons, electric-light balloons, substitutes for gunpowder,

methods of preventing counterfeiting, and so on, sifting out
the promising from the incredibly bad. He offered strong
support to those he felt had useful ideas, as in the case of the
man who had invented a quantity bread-making machine
that could be used with advantage by the Army. He sponsored
a public demonstration of it and afterward gave a reception
for distinguished guests in his apartment to meet the inventor.[11]

Mrs. Henry and some of her friends founded a home for
newsboys. The first conscription acts were passed, ones which
could be avoided by paying three hundred dollars for a sub-
stitute, and the cause of hard feeling. Mary and her sisters
read "Frankenstein" and went to visit the Gillisses at the Observatory by way of roads that were totally liquid. Some
Plains Indians came on a visit to the Great White Father
and Lincoln held a reception for them, at which Professor
Henry diffused a little knowledge by explaining a globe to
them. The Indians listened to him gravely.

On April 1, 1863, a new Confederate raider put to sea to
join that dreaded commerce destroyer the *Alabama*. The
new ship was the *Georgia*, and it was rumored that the traitor
Maury was commanding it.

On April 7 a Union fleet of monitors attempted to take
Charleston by water, and ran afoul of the mines that had
been slung from ropes across the entrance to the harbor. The
Keokuk was lost to the infernal machines, and the traitor
Maury was cursed in public. The National Academy of Sciences went so far as to pass a measure condemning the Wind
and Current Charts. Joseph Henry refused to join in the
attacks on Maury, writing to Bache that the torpedo just
wasn't worth a formal condemnation.[12]

Toward the middle of April the Army of the Potomac, now
under Fighting Joe Hooker, who looked and talked the
part, set out for Richmond again. Lee's army, about half

216

as big as Hooker's, waited again across the Rappahannock. Hooker took off into the Wilderness in an effort to flank Lee. He came back after finally fighting at Chancellorsville and losing.

"Old Joe Hooker, come *out* of the Wilderness!" urchins on the streets in Washington sang derisively as again the defeated army returned.

Once more the long rows of ambulances moved down to the wharfs at the foot of Sixth Street and came back loaded with the wounded. Stonewall Jackson, shot in the confusion of the fighting in the Wilderness, was dead. Meade replaced Hooker in the long succession of Union commanders.

The Henry family went to Princeton for Mary Alexander's wedding but had to hurry home on the eighteenth of June because it looked as if Lee was getting ready to invade the North again. During their absence a baby had been abandoned at the Smithsonian and the Patterson girls had kept it. Naturally Harriet wouldn't think of turning it over to the authorities. When Joseph wrote on June 25, 1863 to Professor Bache, who had in a sudden panic gone off to Philadelphia to prepare the town's defenses, they still had the infant and there were no complaints. The town was full of the wee things this spring, soldiers, women, and war being what they are. Washington had always been noted for its bawdy houses, and before the war it had had an estimated 500 prostitutes. Now everyone said there were that many houses (called "ranches"). The painted creatures were everywhere, and made parts of town once considered respectable, such as Pennsylvania Avenue, now quite beyond the pale. Ladies shopped at the better shops up the hill on Seventh Street and avoided the Avenue. Sometimes they came home and found babies on the doorstep. Many tiny bodies were found floating in the canal and broken by the roadway where a constant stream of horses passed. The better people of the town demanded that the loose women be ousted. They weren't.

Before Gettysburg (July 1–4, 1863), during the battle and after it, the town was so close to the fighting, and so many stray troop units of all sorts were charging everywhere, that Washington seemed almost infiltrated with rebels. Dorothea Dix came to dinner and told the Henrys that friends of hers had seen men they knew to be members of Lee's army at the theater the night before. Others were seen buying goods in the stores, openly, in worn old homespun without insignia, looking like back-country farmers. Minor raids were reported taking place in the suburbs. Again the war drew in toward Washington. But on Sunday, July 5, after a nervous, waiting Fourth, it was learned that Meade had won a great victory at Gettysburg. Tuesday there came news of the fall of Vicksburg. Washington went mad. They fired hundred-gun salutes and gave three groans for Jeff Davis and passed along the rumor that now Meade had come down with acute indecisiveness, that malady so common to the federal command, and was not following Lee's army. Even though delayed by a flood, Lee still got away. Lincoln looked upon Meade with a disaffection born of too many promises gone astray, so much so that he could almost believe in the treachery of the man. This George Gordon Meade was the engineer, one who had come to the attention of Joseph Henry while a young man, and been begged by the professor to give up the army as a career. With 20,000 casualties at Gettysburg, Lee safe in Virginia, Lincoln as upset as anyone ever saw him, and the North a hotbed of conscription riots and copperheads, Meade might well have remembered Joseph Henry's advice. But he commanded the Army of the Potomac until the war's end, although Grant was soon to assume command of all the armies.

Meade took up quarters in the field, along the Rappahannock in Virginia, and Washington lost some of its armed-

camp look. The earthwork forts were still there, very thinly
manned, and a token handful of men took care of the bridge
approaches. There were plenty of soldiers in town, being on
leave, convalescents, "hopeless stragglers" (who were supposed to stay in their camp near Alexandria), and those on
the endless Army details. In the field short, sharp cavalry
clashes took place, the Orange and Alexandria railroad lines
were cut and repaired, not much happening in Virginia this
winter. The news, and "Great and Glorious News" it was,
came from Lookout Mountain and Missionary Ridge, and at
least important news from Chickamauga. No one could be
daunted now. They were beginning to believe in victory with
assurance for the first time.

Between battles this fall the paper reported large crowds
attending Dr. John Lord's lecture on the fall of the Roman
Empire at the Smithsonian. Miss Kate Chase married Senator Sprague and rather put Washington society's eye out.
In police court Miss Anna Maria Branson, age twenty, and
Miss Ann Cavanoe, age nineteen, of Fighting Alley in South
Washington, were charged with stealing a pair of pants and
a coat from a mercantile establishment. They appeared in
court in wrappers, with lacy white underwear plainly visible,
and told the judge they'd taken the stuff because they felt
like it. The judge sternly asked them what they did for
a living. " '———,' " said the *Star* in reporting their reply. "Shame!" "Hush!" cried the bailiff and the spectators. "Well, you asked me a question and I answered
it," Anna Maria replied. "Three years!" said the judge.
The girls left with a "gross exclamation" directed at the
judge. The *Star* lamented that they were Washington girls
and not exotics attracted by the war.

There was a smallpox epidemic this fall in Washington.
Even Lincoln had it, fortunately a mild case.[13] Mary and
Nell Henry were sent away to the Wyoming Valley, finding

the coal-mine area indescribably picturesque, and Carrie and Harriet went to Princeton. Joseph made a couple of short trips on lighthouse matters, but spent most of his time at the Smithsonian. He wrote Harriet how crowded the town was as the season wore on, and that one of the new places on the Avenue had been named the Smithsonian Restaurant. He missed his family very much, used to being fussed over. Harriet was still small, dark-haired, attractive; very like Mary but without the stern expression with which Mary denied that there was any romance in her practical nature. Well, there were three servants in the house to look after a very absent-minded professor.

At Ford's Theater, John Wilkes Booth was playing in *Richard III*. The *Star* gave him extravagant praise.[14] It was the man as seen, not as remembered a year and a half later, when everyone could recall seeing the canker. He stayed on for two weeks, "electrifying" his audiences.

Mosby's men were raiding close to town this fall. The *Star* referred to them as a gang of shirt-stealing highwaymen who came from good families and *should know better*.

When Lincoln was well enough, a quiet reception was given at the White House for the officers of the visiting Russian fleet. To welcome the New Year the President had the customary open house, receiving first hundreds of Army and Navy officers, then a mad crush of swells and nobodies, some of whom climbed in the windows. The usual exhausting time was had by all. But 1864 looked like a year of promise; a certain cheer seemed to be in the atmosphere.

There was not such a heavy lecture program at the Smithsonian this season, and by no means the activity there had been in the theaters the previous year. The soldiers were in the field, the epidemic was not believed eradicated although thousands of vaccinations were given, and social life generally was confined more to private entertainment.

220

Henry and the War in Washington (Part Two)

In 1864 Joseph Henry kept busy with his boards and committees, but he was never too busy for the struggling inventor, or for his recently returned family, or for his friends. Alexander Dallas Bache had been very unwell of late, attributing his multitude of ills to overwork; Henry knew well enough that his symptoms were of a more serious nature although he refrained from saying anything. Added to Bache's persistent headaches now were a numbness in his right hand and a marked difficulty in expressing himself, both of which seemed to be getting worse. Bache was a large man, almost as tall as Henry, with merry eyes, thin hair plastered closely to his head, and long, thick whiskers. Their friendship was so deep and abiding, and they knew all each other's business so intimately that no one thought it odd that Henry was now so much at the Coast Survey discussing the work there with Bache's subordinates, and assisting Bache all he could.

On February 18, 1864, there was a meeting of the permanent commission, Bache, Henry, and Davis still going by that name, at which they investigated three inventions. Two of these were new types of ironclads, and the other was a means of raising sunken vessels. On February 25 there was a meeting of the Lighthouse Board to investigate the use of a new hydrocarbon as an illuminant. They decided against it, as the substance was too dangerous. Even the fumes would explode. It was called gasoline.[15]

The Confederate commerce raiders sank 257 ships of the Union registry and caused insurance rates to rise so that 700 additional American ships were transferred to foreign registries. They succeeded in ruining American commerce on the high seas for fifty years. These "pirates" were so hated in the North that people paled when their names were mentioned. If they could have gotten their hands on Raphael Semmes, commander of the *Alabama*, he would have been hanged without trial.

Joseph Henry remembered Semmes as a rather peppery naval officer with stiff-waxed mustaches, who had been an inspector of lighthouses. He and his large family had lived near the Navy Yard with their slaves, eight or nine of them.[16] The *Star* referred to him invariably as "the pirate Semmes." Charles Wilkes had been put in charge of a "flying squadron" with the duty of catching the *Alabama* and her sister ships as well as blockade duty among the Caribbean islands. He continued his habitual dictatorial highhandedness, taking over any ships of the federal command that came in his area, and at last he seized the *Vanderbilt*, the supposed fastest ship afloat, which had been ordered to follow the *Alabama* everywhere she went. When at last ordered to release the *Vanderbilt*, it missed the *Alabama* at Cape Town by five days, and Wilkes was ordered back to Washington. Even then the Navy Department was willing to forget about it, but Wilkes had no control over his tongue. This spring of 1864 he was court-martialed and found guilty of disobedience, disrespect, insubordination, and of conduct unbecoming an officer. He was reprimanded and suspended for three years.

The Battle of the Wilderness started on May 5, 1864, and during it the forces under Grant, who had taken command of the Union armies in March, were badly defeated and yet proceeded to pursue Lee on to Spotsylvania Court House as if they had won, and so broke the evil spell of fight, pause, fight, pause. With Grant it was fight all the time.

This was the horrible month, when the wounded, screaming, and helpless, burned to death in the great forest fire that followed the battle in the Wilderness; when Grant said, "I propose to fight it out on this line, if it takes all summer"; when the boy cadets from the Virginia Military Institute gained the battle colors which their flags bear to this day, fighting and winning at New Market; when J. E. B. Stuart was mortally wounded at Yellow Tavern—and while we were thus engaged, Maximilian of Hapsburg landed at Vera Cruz and proclaimed himself Emperor of Mexico.

In the beginning of June the war went on as it had before. Many loyal people in the North began to wonder if it was worth it. "As He died to make men holy, let us die to make men free" had not been written by a soldier, they reminded each other. After Cold Harbor they were calling Grant a butcher, and he was content to besiege Petersburg, having lost almost as many men since he took over the Union army as there were men in the Confederate army. Lincoln had been renominated for president on June 7, 1864, with Andrew Johnson, the pro-Union Democrat from Tennessee, as vice president. It would not be easy to elect them with so much dissension, it was feared. On June 19, 1864, the rebel raider *Alabama* was sunk off Cherbourg by the federal steam frigate *Kearsarge*. To the Union's rage the pirate Semmes and most of his crew were picked up by a private British yacht, the *Deerhound*, captained by John Lancaster of the Royal Yacht Club, and carried safely off to England.[17]

Came July, 1864. "Rebels a-marchin' on Washington!" the newsboys began to shout.

Jubal Early had taken his "rebel band" and marched on Frederick, Maryland, about thirty miles north of Washington on July 6. Lew Wallace, who later was to write *Ben Hur*, tried to stop him on the banks of the Monocacy but failed. On July 11 Early was at Silver Spring, a Maryland suburb of Washington, with 14,000 men. Official Washington went into a flap. Grant had taken almost every able-bodied man with him into the Wilderness. Henry's friend General Meigs produced 2,000 civilian employees from the Quartermaster Department to fight, convalescents were hauled out, some stale District militia and some unmounted cavalry started for Silver Spring, stragglers were pressed into service, a scratch cavalry outfit was mounted, one artillery battalion was located, and all the employees of the Navy, including professors, set out to defend the town's almost abandoned earthworks.

Harriet came back from shopping to complain that Seventh Street was so crowded with refugees from nearby Maryland that it was impossible to cross it. A Mr. Shaad came in and said the rebels were fighting at Tennally Town and at Fort Moss [18] out on Seventh Street. The Smithsonian family went up on the tallest tower, Mr. De Bust thoughtfully bringing his glass, to watch. They stayed there until dark, seeing the sun set on a scene of quiet beauty, staring with the telescope at the signalman waving his flags on top of the Soldiers' Home, watching some colored troops moving slowly down Twelfth Street, and at the lengthening shadows of the towers on the grass. Henry drove into the city but returned at ten o'clock, reporting all quiet.

The civilian population was so cool as to appear bored the next day, although cannon fire almost drowned out the rattle of the new horsecars. Ladies doing their shopping on Seventh Street waited impatiently for horse-drawn batteries to clatter past. The day's program at the Smithsonian went off as planned. That afternoon three brigades of the Sixth Corps, generously spared by Grant, arrived at the Sixth Street wharfs and marched toward Silver Spring. They were obviously veterans, and underneath the air of regarding all this as a nuisance, the loyal hearts of Washington beat a little faster, seeing them. The secesh booed and got away with it.

Sight-seeing, considered in poor taste ever since First Bull Run, took on a certain acceptableness. After all, Manassas was thirty miles away. *This* was right here. Even Lincoln got up on a parapet at Fort Stevens to ogle the gray army. Crowds were turned back at the end of Seventh Street (where it became Seventh Street Road) without seeing any rebels except some prisoners, and nobody paid attention to prisoners any more unless they were Mosby's men and then nobody did much except fling rocks and yell, "Hang them!" There was no news except rumors; they had to make what they could out of the sound of firing. The Navy, under still-sprightly sixty-year-old Admiral Goldsborough, marched off to Fort Lincoln, which commanded the road to Bladensburg, stayed a few hours, and then marched back. Simon Newcomb felt remarkably silly since they were so obviously useless as fighters.

The next day Early and his men, who could have disrupted Washington if they had attacked on the eleventh, were gone. Henry took Mary and Caroline on a drive to the "theater of the late conflict," finding all desolation. Houses were burned or just torn apart, gardens trampled, fields torn up, fences down, orchards cut to pieces by shellfire, everything with the wrecked look that says war has been here. While most of the local people were yelling for Jubal Early's blood, Joseph Henry was attempting to aid a rebel doctor who had remained behind with seventeen seriously wounded men who were without medical supplies, food, or shelter. While her father was arranging for ambulances to take them to Lincoln hospital, where the other Confederate wounded had been taken, Mary wandered around and read the messages scribbled on the walls of the nearby houses, one of which was signed, *The Biggest Rebel of Them All.* The messages were not allowed to sully the pure pages of her diary. She did note that the rebel doctor was very noble in appearance and manner.

The summer was almost unbearably hot. The grounds of the Smithsonian scorched, the smells could have been cut with a knife, and mosquito nets had to be provided for the patients in the hospital next door. At night they tried various forms of oxyhydrogenous limelight as a means of sending code signals from the towers of the Smithsonian to the signal station on the roof at the Soldiers' Home. A female sub-marine inventor [19] finally became so obnoxious that Henry had to leave town on lighthouse business to get away from her. He took Mary and Carrie with him to Shelter Island while Harriet and Nell went on to Germantown. After that he went to visit Bache at his survey camp, finding him in somewhat improved health, and then to his favorite spot, Staten Island Lighthouse Depot. The rest of the family went to Princeton.

In a mellow mood he wrote Bache that all things prospered with which he was connected. However, he felt that the government had been cheated on the construction of the sea wall at Staten Island, having been charged twice what it was worth and gotten a shoddy job, too. And the honest man confided to Bache that his expenditures for the past year had exceeded his salary by $400, although they had watched every cent.[20] It was nice to have one's best friend on the Board of Regents: the following year his salary was increased to $4,500. He had previously refused one raise; perhaps since then he had been nagged at to be practical until it finally sank in.

The dirty political campaign was despaired over by the Henrys, and Mary was unable to see why anyone should fight so desperately for the honor of having a terrible war blamed on them. She could say, "Poor man, I pitied him intensely," when she saw Lincoln riding in an open barouche, looking sad and tired, headed into town from the Soldiers' Home, which he used as a kind of summer White House, away from the pestilential vapors of the canal. But when he ran for re-election he was "a boor and totally incompetent." Neither was McClellan fitted for the position, she felt. Her father, bound by his position, could not take sides in all honor, but his admiration for Lincoln had never wavered once he had

226

gotten past the Washington view of the man which his family shared.

It was very gratifying to Professor Henry that rainy, foggy night when men were trotting about with their "trowsers" rolled up, clustered under umbrellas, waiting for the election results to come in by telegraph, to hear the triumphant chorus of "Rally Round the Flag!" [21] Another term for the man he could not feel toward as he felt toward others, who demolished his detachment and struck at his heart. He wished him well, there in his tall-towered castle, grander by far than any other residence in Washington, the rain pouring down upon the slated roof, past the mullioned windows and all the wonders safe inside. [22]

Sherman marched to the sea. Savannah was a Christmas present to the Union, and Georgia lay wrecked behind him. "Custar" was the golden-haired cavalry hero, even though his flowing locks were nearly as red as his perpetually sunburned face. Petersburg was still under siege, all avoiding the gap of the "Crater," that long-tunneled failure of the previous summer. Professor Agassiz came on one of his always-welcome visits for Christmas of 1864, still unsuccessfully trying to talk Joseph out of his belief in Darwinism. But they got along so splendidly, these two brilliant men, their talk set off such sparks in each other, that everyone loved to see them together. After Agassiz left, the crop of crackpot inventors almost got out of hand. One bushy-haired fellow wanted to suspend a telegraphic cable across the Atlantic by balloons. Mrs. Farnum, the lady submarine inventor, was much incensed over Henry's refusal to recommend her submarine to the government. The limelight lanterns which flashed Morse code were turned over to the Signal Corps.

On January 24, 1865, Henry and his clerical assistant,

William Rhees, were working intently over some papers in Henry's office in the main tower. Some workmen were remodeling the picture gallery and since they were having a particularly cold spell, a stove had been set up for them. The flue into which the stovepipe had been let was supposed to be safe and the professor had asked about it several times, to the workmen's amusement. Harriet and the two younger girls were in their apartment. Mary was in the library reading. It was a little before 3:00 P.M.

Suddenly a piece of ceiling material fell on Henry's desk. He and Rhees, startled, looked at it in amazement. It was *burning*. And then upon their absent-minded ears burst the terrifying roaring and crackling of a great fire, clouds of smoke swept past the windows, a crashing sounded as of falling floors.

The Smithsonian was going up in flames.[23]

NOTES TO CHAPTER ELEVEN

1. Mary Henry's diary, December 25, 1862.
2. *Photographic History of the Civil War.*
3. *Woman's Work in the Civil War,* Brockett and Vaughn.
4. *Joseph Henry, A Memorial.* Quoted by Simon Newcomb.
5. *Ibid.*
6. *Ibid.*
7. The Emancipation Proclamation mentioned earlier was a preliminary one to test out the feeling of the country, issued after Antietam.
8. All Negro slaves didn't take their condition lying down. In order to make their existence easier, to get some of that vital "kick" out of life, they fought the little war against their masters. Good white people refused to believe in the little war:

the Negro was too stupid. Example: Frank Minor loaned
Maury his old gardener Louis White for a while to get the
vegetable garden at the Observatory in shape. White wanted
to go back home. He put on his best stupid expression and
pulled up all the asparagus plants. No slave beater, Maury
sent him home as being too useless to have around. In her diary
Mary Boykin Chesnut tells of similar episodes with slaves, one
of whom almost killed her with an overdose of medicine "ac-
cidentally."

9. Mary Henry's diary.

10. *Joseph Henry, His Life and Works*, Coulson.

11. Mary Henry's diary, February 14, 1863.

12. January 22, 1864.

13. The *Star* of December 6, 1863, admitted to his indis-
position.

14. *Star*, November 3, 1863.

15. Notes and papers of Joseph Henry at the Smithsonian.

16. 1860 Census.

17. *Records of the Union and Confederate Navies, Series
I, Vol. III*. Mr. Lancaster said as his racing yacht passed the
Kearsarge that Captain Winslow called to him, "For God's
sake, save them!" Seeing that the *Alabama* was going fast and
the Yankees seemed little disposed to pick up survivors, Lancaster proceeded to do so. His refusal to turn his guests over to
Captain Winslow almost caused that chubby fellow to have
apoplexy.

18. This is from Mary Henry's diary. Probably she meant
Fort Stevens. Her spelling of Tenleytown was the one in use
in her day.

19. Letter from Joseph Henry to Alexander Dallas Bache,
August 21, 1864, at the Smithsonian.

20. September 25, 1864.

21. *Star*, November 9, 1864.

22. There was a plank from a redwood tree, a sarcopha-
gus, a copy in marble of the Dying Gladiator, according to the

229

CHAPTER TWELVE

Maury and the Civil War in England

To ARRIVE IN England in this late fall of 1862 was to find a country that had those cures for excessive democracy so dear to Matthew Fontaine Maury's heart. He thought the aristocracy should rule: well, here they did. Out of seven and a half million men of voting age less than one million could vote. Groups of powerful interests smugly ran the country by their influence and connections with this voting class. One of the most powerful of these factions was the great textile manufacturing group and its shareholders, owners of bleacheries, dye works, spinning mills, and weaving mills centered at Manchester. In nearby Liverpool, along the Mersey, were the great cotton warehouses, whose owners, dealers in raw cotton, were closely allied with the textile manufacturers.

When the Civil War started there was a three-year supply of cotton in these warehouses.[1] After a decent interval the warehouses were padlocked, the textile industry shut down—

and the price of cotton skyrocketed. At the time of Maury's arrival in England cotton was $200 a bale, and the bread-line had been invented.

If England had decided to support the Confederacy, the Yankee textile industry and the great experiment in running a country by the vote of the many both might have been destroyed, certainly very seriously damaged. But the Crimean War was still a bad taste in the British people's mouths, they had a vast merchant shipping to protect, India was in a serious state of upheaval, and John Bright was stirring up the laboring classes with ideas that hurt the South. While the ruling class waited, making money on cotton and Confederate shipbuilding contracts, the luck of the South turned. New Orleans was lost, and Lee had to fall back after Antietam. As the South failed in the war, so its prestige faded abroad.

October 7, 1862, had heard Gladstone say in a most heartening speech that the Confederacy had made a nation. Maury wrote a glowing picture of the South in a letter that was printed (after some judicious editing) in the *Times* of December 22, 1862. But even this could not stand up against the Emancipation Proclamation with which Lincoln started off the new year. Shortly after news of it reached England Newman Hall made a speech at a grand emancipation rally in London in which he referred to slavery as a foul conspiracy against civilization, humanity, and God, and deplored that the representative of the Confederacy should ever kiss the "pure, matronly, and widowed hand" of their queen. The crowd roared its agreement.

After meeting Captain James D. Bulloch, the other Confederate naval commissioner for England, at Fraser and Trenholm's office at 10 Rumford Place, Liverpool, Maury had to go on to dirty, dreary London, where he and Matsy set up in two rooms at Mrs. Hopkinson's, 10 Sackville Street. Here Matsy went to school, and ran errands to James M.

Mason's place on Upper Seymour Street, and took a walk every afternoon with his pa, except when the fog was so bad they had to stay home with the candles lit. Confederate naval officers were always around and coaches with crests on the doors waited outside. Here Maury met for the first time one of his closest friends and warmest admirers, with whom he had been corresponding for years, Marin Jansen of the Netherlands Navy. Jansen was a big man, bold-faced, mild-eyed, who had done great work of his own in oceanography and who had been much quoted by Maury in *The Physical Geography of the Sea.* He had translated Maury's book into Dutch and was a Confederate sympathizer. When Jansen came over from Delft they had to celebrate. They took Matsy to the Zoo. When Jansen left to go on an inspection tour of British shipyards as a guest of the Crown, he gave Matsy a five-pound note and promised his pa to keep his eye open for any ships that might be converted into cruisers for the Confederacy.[2]

Maury and the South needed another *Alabama*, which, like the *Florida*, had been built by Laird's in Liverpool to British naval specifications for a steam sloop. Barring this, Maury's ideal would have been a ship of less than fifteen feet draft, good under canvas and very fast under steam, capable of staying at sea a year.[3] Owing to the pressure of time and public opinion no more were built, and the Confederate commissioners noted with dismay that Union ambassador to England Charles Francis Adams had his eye on the steam rams Laird's was now building for them. The British liked to see Confederate commerce destroyers launched, since these ships were burning or scaring the great American shipping industry right off the oceans. Ever ready to make what they could out of the great American debacle without getting into it themselves, the British shipping interests did everything they could to hoodwink Adams and his spies and get

merchant ships converted to Confederate commerce destroyers. These ships had a dual mission, to destroy Yankee shipping and draw warships away from the blockade to chase
them. This latter has been claimed a failure, but the Official
Records [4] lists 78 ships delegated to chasing the Confederate
cruisers and blockade runners in just one year, and those
ships all the way from the mighty *Colorado* with its 52 guns
to the tiny *Moccasin* with its three.

Maury was much in demand as a dinner guest, especially
with the Church of England people and those of the aristocracy currently out of power. Reverend Dr. F. W. Tremlett
was willingly enlisted as an aid in Maury's efforts to stir up
pro-Confederate feeling, and it was *former* Foreign Secretary
Lord Malmesbury who asked Maury and Matsy to visit and
then made fun of Matsy for saying, "Yes, sir" and "No,
ma'am," which bothered Matsy not at all since he knew
Virginia manners were right manners.

Along with his other work Maury was kept busy with his
commissions of things to buy for the folks at home—the first
consignment of which was lost when the blockade runner
Royal Princess was caught in February 1863.[5] He began to
have a series of nightmares, all more or less on the same theme:
children and friends mutilated, dying, dead.[6]

It had been a long time since he had heard from home, and
when he had left, Johnny (his Davy Jones) had been a
prisoner of war. Rutson and his sister Ann did everything
they could to forward Maury's letters in and out of the
beleaguered South. When the flag-of-truce boats were running it was easier, but still Mat got his mail in dribbles or
batches, as luck would have it. Johnny had been exchanged
long before his father knew it, although he heard that his
family had been forced to evacuate "the burg" again and
scatter, some to Bowling Green,[7] some to Richmond, and that
most of their furniture and other possessions had been lost.

While they were suffering the hardships of war and blockade he and Matsy were watching the great illumination of London in honor of the wedding of the Prince of Wales and the regal Danish princess Alexandra.

In March of 1863 Maury succeeded in buying on the Clyde what he thought was an excellent ship for a cruiser, the new iron steamship *Japan*, 560 tons, brig-rigged. After sundry difficulties he succeeded in sailing her away from under Charles Francis Adams's Yankee nose without getting so much publicity that the British government would have to save face by stopping him. Off Newhaven, on April 1, 1863, the *Japan* became the *C.S.S. Georgia*, meeting an escort loaded with guns and ammunition, and a set of Confederate officers for her scratch crew. Captain of the *Georgia* was William Lewis Maury, one of Mat's cousins who had helped with the mine laying in the James and who was married to Ann and Rutson Maury's niece, Nan. The Maury name led Yankees to believe that Mat was the captain.

All the intriguing and plotting and secret meeting, the taking of papers under false names, the frantic efforts to cover their tracks, the red-tape snarls with the Confederate government—for a ship that turned out no better than the *Georgia!* The only thing wrong with the *Georgia* was that she wouldn't sail. The *Alabama* was another *Flying Cloud* in her admirers' eyes, and she actually spent most of her time under sail and even made some of her spectacular chases and escapes under sail. Of course "Old Beeswax" Semmes could have made a sailing ship out of a breadboard and a dough cloth, they said. But the *Georgia* was forever having to put into port to coal up; friendly ports were getting scarce and Union warships were common enough now to afford to lie in wait for the rebel cruisers. The *Georgia* managed to sink only a disputed eight or nine ships during a year's cruise in the Atlantic. Maury reminded Samuel Barron in Paris, chief of the Confederate naval commissioners, that the *Georgia* got her orders from Richmond, not from him.

While visiting at Worthy Hall in Sheffield on April 8, 1863, Maury got a black-edged letter from his cousin Robert Maury. It was a letter of condolence on the death of Johnny, his beloved Davy Jones, again missing at Vicksburg and now believed dead. Maury, always at the mercy of his emotions, went into a state of shock. Numbly he and Matsy moved to Bowdon, near Manchester and Liverpool, where a former tutor of the lost Davy Jones, Mr. Micklejohn, had Rose Hill school for boys, and where Matsy was enrolled. Every letter Maury wrote showed that all of his thoughts were on his lost son.

Dabney had kept too close a watch over Johnny. He found himself in the midst of battles looking around for his young cousin to see that he was all right, he would always be finding reasons to send him to the rear, to keep him from harm. After Johnny was captured and released without parole Dabney renewed his efforts to see that nothing happened to him. And Johnny smiled that young, heart-rending smile of his and slipped away on every occasion, refusing to be mollycoddled. He could take care of himself. On the morning of Tuesday, January 27, 1863, he had gone off alone on horseback to prowl along the Mississippi. His riderless horse came back, but that happened to all of them, and was the subject of much joking. However, when he hadn't shown up by the following morning Dabney took one of his Texans, Colonel Burnett, a renowned tracker, and set off to look for Johnny. They found where his gray mare had crossed a deep branch of a bayou and on the other side signs of a struggle, bits of paper cartridge, and evidence that several men and a small boat had been there. That Johnny had stumbled alone on a Union scouting party and had been captured for the second time

seemed plainly shown. Relieved, they returned to camp and
Dabney sent his adjutant under a flag of truce to Grant's
camp to inquire for him. To their alarm Grant knew nothing
of Johnny's capture, nor did Admiral Porter who was there
with him, commanding the Union fleet in the river. So Johnny
vanished into the world of rumor and conjecture and was
never seen again. Possibly he was that young Confederate
officer who died a couple of days later on one of the Union
gunboats of pneumonia. He might have been robbed and
murdered and thrown in the river by the scouts who captured
him. Dabney, to whom Johnny was the most lovable, unforgettable person he had ever known, seemed to sense that the
boy was dead but he never stopped trying to locate him.

Dabney could not tell his "dear Aunt Ann" so he wrote to
her brother Brodie Herndon, who was a doctor, and asked
him to tell her. None of the immediate family could get up
their nerve to tell Mat and Matsy over the sea. After all, they
kept telling themselves, perhaps Johnny would turn up. And
so an ordinary letter of condolence, written a month after
Johnny's death, told Maury the sad news.

He was never the same after Johnny died. Something went
wrong that never was to be set right, as if his wildfire emotions were burning up something deep inside. For months his
letters were all of his Davy Jones, remembering the small
episodes of his life; once it had hurt him to see Matsy wearing
Dave's shabby old coat, but now it was precious to him, as if
seeing Dave in it. Over and over his precious, sleeping boy;
tormenting himself, remembering times he had hurt the boy's
feelings by laughing at his lisp. Telling his wife how much he
appreciated her courage, lamenting that they could not be
together.

Rutson Maury and his sister and even old Mr. Hasbrouck
all but moved heaven and earth trying to locate Johnny in

a federal prison or hospital. They came up with a heartbreaking array of lies, hoaxes, sensation hunters, and distant Maury relations.

Crushed by the boy's death, unable to get money or men from the Confederate government to buy and man ships that he did locate, Maury stumbled along in his efforts in behalf of the Confederacy, trying to enlist Jansen's help in designing an ironclad ram,[8] complaining about the close watch kept on him by Adams's spies, about the conflicting orders that kept him from accomplishing anything. At night he dreamed of Davy Jones, looking frail and pale, his eyes so clear a blue that Maury was suddenly awake, shivering. He sent more packages home, telling the family sternly not to complain if they were lost; that they knew what real loss was now. And every time he looked out the window at the English countryside he saw—peace.[9]

There was no hope for the Confederacy in this land.

The most serious enemy the South had in England was not Viscount Palmerston, the Prime Minister, nor was it Lord John Russell, the Foreign Secretary. The man who made the most trouble for them was an eloquent Quaker, a spinning-mill owner of Rochdale in Lancashire and member of Parliament for Birmingham. John Bright had the ear of the lower middle classes and the working classes; the unemployed workers in the British textile industry were kept well informed on the terrors of slavery by his emotional speeches. He knew that the British upper classes wanted to keep the vote from these laborers, and he was determined that they should fail. If the Union was dissolved there was no hope for the growth of democracy in England. The aristocracy would continue to run the government. He dwelt at length on the sufferings of the slaves in his speeches, sparing nothing to make the half-starved working classes demand that the blockade *not* be

238

broken. He gave them a great incentive to bear their privations: that man might be free.

From early 1862 until early 1865 about $20,000,000 was spent on public relief in the cotton-famine areas, mostly around Manchester. Living in nearby Bowdon, Maury saw these starving people. He never mentioned them.

The high prices led to the growing of cotton in greater quantity in India and Egypt and to the start of its cultivation in other places such as Brazil. By the end of the war the British mills were operating part time, with about 40 per cent of their usual supply of cotton fibers.

Back home the family was now living in the old house which the University of Virginia had used as an infirmary; what a crowd gathered—cousins, aunts, nieces, nephews, sisters, in-laws, all to eat boiled shin and corn bread and be glad for that. They sent Maury and Matsy a package that got through the blockade safely: chinquapins, that burr-clad nut so plentiful in the Virginia woods and tasting like all the world's nothings rolled into one.

In November Maury bought a condemned British dispatch boat, the *Victor*, which had even more wrong with it than the *Georgia*, and named it the *Rappahannock*. Wont to bluster about the great ships he would acquire if only he had the money, when he did get the money, he bought junk. The *Rappahannock* got to sea but at once had to put into Calais for emergency repairs and there she stayed. The *Georgia*, supposed to have rendezvoused with the *Rappahannock*, had to put into Bordeaux for a chilly reception, and finally crept into Liverpool.

Maury would leave nothing unattempted that might hurt the Union. Knowing the British and French hatred of the Monroe Doctrine, he began to encourage the Ferdinand Maximilian plan to seize Mexico. He wrote Maximilian assurances of Confederate friendship, in the hope of getting French concessions for the Confederacy. Maximilian, however, took all of Maury's flattery as only his due; he would take over the Mexican government as a favor to the poor people of that country. Maury kept on with his correspondence, hoping he would be able to use Maximilian in some way.

He sent home large boxes for Christmas in 1863 and spent his days uneventfully at Bowdon this winter, doing a lot of letter writing and *Times* reading, having a little brandy with his lunch, watching Matsy nap on the hearth rug after dinner, looking terribly like his lost Davy Jones. He wrote to his family his fears for the future of their country, to everyone else that things looked bright now for the Confederacy. He even suggested to his cousin Frank Minor (not being alone in this) that a possible union with France might be preferable to groveling under the heel of a victorious North. Despondent, he thought of his children growing up without him. In the spring he fell sick, although this was carefully kept from his family and only showed in his correspondence with Dr. Tremlett and Marin Jansen.

The *Georgia* had proved so useless as a commerce destroyer that she was sold to Edwin Bates of Liverpool on June 1, 1864. In June Maury took Matsy with him to Paris on business for the Confederacy, to see Slidell and Samuel Barron about the ships being built there. He found time to walk along the Seine and think of Davy Jones. Then, ill again, he had to make a hurried return.

Back in England, while he was still not himself but feeling better, the *Alabama* was sunk by the *Kearsarge* in a curiously one-sided battle. Standing by as if to insure fair play was the British racing yacht *Deerhound*, which dashed in after the battle and picked up Captain Semmes and most of his crew and triumphantly carried them off to Southampton and turned them loose instead of letting the Yankees hang them.

Dr. Tremlett and Mr. Mason went down to Southampton and brought Captain Semmes to London, where much was made over him. But no new ship was forthcoming. Captain Semmes started back to Richmond by blockade runner, still with a rope around his neck, but got through safely. Maury, ill, discouraged, worried about his family, stayed on uselessly in England. Mallory would give him no orders. Glumly he followed the progress of the war in the *Times*, telling himself it was all lies, feeling that it was true.

Dick was wounded again, shot through the hips at Drewry's Bluff, and after some fear that he would never walk again was up and limping around. Naturally, his mother was the first to get there to nurse him after his injury. And this when Dick's wife would come to see "dear Mama" only if her best girl friend was asked also (despite there being barely enough food for the family) because she felt her husband's sisters didn't like her. Poor Susan: her affectations included referring to lunch as "the matin meal," to Dick as "my lord," and to her father-in-law as "sire." No wonder Betty and Nannie loathed her: she didn't know any better than to take the Victorian novel seriously. When she had a baby boy shortly after Johnny's death she named the child Matthew Fontaine instead of John Herndon, the usual mark of respect for a recently-dead relative, and was accused of playing for her "sire's" favor.

This was the summer of 1864, the summer of the siege of Petersburg, of Grant in Virginia, of bloody battles, and constantly advancing blue-clad soldiers.

Maury contrived to form a "Society for the Cessation of Hostilities in America," with Dr. Tremlett as his front. They got to see Lord Palmerston, the Prime Minister, who couldn't see his way clear to interfere.

The story of Maury's *Rappahannock*, tied up in Calais, was a sad one. The unfortunate little vessel was commanded by Charles Fauntleroy, Lieutenant, C.S.N., who was forever being insulted. No matter who, or how, everyone with whom he came in contact was rude and attempted to offend. If he had been as pugnacious as he was prickly the *Rappahannock* might have had some adventures, but all his endeavor was to keep her in port and embroiled in red tape, attachments, and court orders. The *Rappahannock* was even put up for sale once by the port authorities after Fauntleroy refused to move her a little way to accommodate another captain and had to cut the other ship's rigging to prevent being run down. When it looked as if she might be ordered to sea despite his efforts, Fauntleroy began complaining to the naval commissioners that her firepower was insufficient and he was afraid of his personal honor being damaged if the ship was unable to fight properly. Instead of replacing Fauntleroy, Barron meekly gave up and sold the *Rappahannock*. What might have happened to this last of Maury's purchases in the hands of another skipper is anybody's guess.[10]

After two operations, the nature of which was described only as "painful," Maury began to feel better although he still felt weak and depressed. Advised to try sea bathing, he and Matsy went to Llandudno, Wales. He had never seen the British institution of the bathing machine and after one amazed look at a lady bather in what looked like a flannel nightgown Mat knew that if laughter could cure, this was the place to come.

By August he was much improved in health and self-esteem. He was informed that his experiments with mines had turned out most successfully on the James, and Secretary of the Navy Mallory told him he could stay in England or return to the Confederacy at his own discretion. The mine war had been going on well in the tributaries of the Mississippi and at Charleston Harbor and other besieged spots, but suddenly the attention of two nations was focused on the mines

in the James. That spring another attempt to take Richmond
by water had been undertaken. In 1862, the guns of Fort
Darling had driven the Yankee warships back. This time
Lieutenant Hunter Davidson had exploded a mine from the
shore, right under the *Commodore Jones*, one of the Union
flotilla, blasting her sky-high and killing 60 of her crew.
The Federals had tried to sneak through anyway, although
warned by "reliable contraband" (runaway slaves) that the
river was protected by mines that could be fired from a distance. The Federals had fallen back. Maury wrote home that
he could send the mining instructions by mail perfectly
easily. He chose to stay in England.

He was doing secret experiments for the British government with land mines, which could also be used as submarine
mines. Working with Wheatstone, inventor of the British
needlepointing telegraph, and others, he rented a field near
Bowdon and proceeded to blow it up. He had a Confederate
patent [11] on a means of exploding mines from the shore that
insured the right ship would be blown up. It was a mathematical computing device with sighting angles, very simple,
but still more accurate than judging by eye. Owing to
Maury's position it all was kept very hushed up, but he got
great quantities of insulated wire and material for batteries
off to the Confederacy this year.

Although the ironclads being built for them in Liverpool
were expropriated, thanks to Adams, another project, the
chief work of the naval commissioners of late, was now rush-
ing to completion in the fall of 1864. This was a steam ram,
the *Sphinx*, which H. Arman de Reviere had been building
for them at Bordeaux. It cost $400,000 compared to the old
Virginia's $50,000, and there were grave and noble hopes
that she might break the blockade at Wilmington. She was a
small but gracefully proportioned ship, great iron prow and
all. After considerable cloak-and-dagger work she was gotten

to Copenhagen and armed with the three British-made Armstrong guns planned for her. Then she was to rendezvous with the blockade runner *City of Richmond* to take on her supplies. Bulloch asked particularly for Hunter Davidson, now a commander, who had helped Maury with the mines and sunk the *Commodore Jones*, to captain the *City of Richmond*. Davidson had to hurry to catch the next dark of the moon, being loaded with material for mines that Maury was sending home and could only run the blockade then. They rendezvoused with the *C.S. Ram Stonewall* (ex-*Sphinx*) at Quiberon on January 24, 1865 but were so continually delayed by storms that the *City of Richmond* had to catch the February dark of the moon. They laid the keel of the *Stonewall* under a bad sign: storms made up on purpose just for her. And Thomas Jefferson Page, her commander, began to lose heart and no one could blame him, despite the prime engineer Maury sent him via the *Louisa Ann Fanny* to help when it was discovered they didn't have a set of plans for the ship and could hardly figure out her workings. Things were going badly indeed at home. Page could plainly see that he would but lead the *Stonewall* to her destruction and all their deaths.[12]

On February 3, 1865, Lincoln met Confederate Vice President Alexander Stephens in Hampton Roads officially to discuss terms of a possible Confederate surrender. But the southerners would not give up their separate nation and Lincoln would not consider peace unless they did, so they parted.

By now the Confederate commerce destroyer *Shenandoah*, launched in October of 1864, had sunk nine ships of the Union merchant and whaling fleets, and was hardly warmed up. Bulloch seemed to have a wonderful eye for ships and sailors. Those of his letters preserved in the Official Records show a man with a million problems, patiently trying to handle them well. The demonstrations of friendship between him and Hunter Davidson, one of the most likable of men, showed him to be a person warm and understandable. He had to bear crushing disappointments.

Back in Virginia, Charlottesville fell to Custer's men in March of 1865. That villainous Custer's soldiers frightened the women at the Infirmary half to death by forcing their way in and demanding food and clothes (women's clothes). Nannie defied them, and her mother gave them everything Nannie had just sworn they didn't have. Nannie didn't believe them when they threatened to burn the house down, but Mrs. Maury wanted to take no chances. Finally, after pleas to the Union command, a guard was provided for the house. Then the soldiers tried to climb in the back windows. The town was wrecked, just by the peaceful occupation, but at least the University and Monticello on its hill overlooking the town were spared. The Maurys were all but destitute.[13]

Lee surrendered on Sunday, April 9, 1865. Unable to realize what was happening, not believing that the end could be *now*, Maury planned to sail for Havana on May 2, 1865, with a load of mine equipment and there transfer to a blockade runner.

Rutson was writing him by every ship to stay in England, fearing that Maury might blunder into Union hands. As a result of his work with the cruisers many who had been Maury's staunchest supporters now denounced him. Rutson sent the Maurys at Charlottesville money and even offered to pay Big Nannie's way to England and all her expenses, adding that she would be welcome at his house as before.

But even in England the Confederates had worn out their welcome. Defeated, they were no longer of any use to the British. When the *Nova Scotia* docked at Liverpool with news of Lincoln's assassination the town hall flag was lowered to half mast and other flags all over town soon followed suit.

The Confederate Club was stoned, angry voices denounced the southerners' revenge, and the whole British nation turned against the South in a moment.[14]

His family and friends wrote Maury repeatedly to stay in England, but he started out for Havana with the material for the submarine mines. Finding there that the bad news was only too true, he left the material and ordered it turned over to Bulloch for disposal, sent Matsy to Rutson in New York, and, remembering his long encouragement of Maximilian, he went on to Mexico.

One of his old enemies of the Retiring Board, S. W. Godon, now admiral of a special squadron sent to catch the *Stonewall* (turned over to the Cuban authorities on May 19, 1865), was sent Maury's letter of surrender by the American consul at Vera Cruz. He forwarded it to Secretary of the Navy Gideon Welles in Washington with a caustic comment: *I enclose herewith a characteristic letter from M. F. Maury, formerly of our Navy, received the day before I left Havana. The rebellion can hardly have well ended without a special parole to that gentleman.*[15]

Maury was like a man stung to death by his own passions, not understanding conditions at home, imagining what he would, determined to have his own way, blind and deaf to every counsel. Rather than submit Matthew Fontaine Maury to the conqueror, he joined the French forces of oppression in Mexico. The Mexicans meant nothing to him as people, or as good or bad; he saw only his carefully cultivated friend Maximilian as an emperor, and as someone who could help him. His own honor was so correct, so nice, that he could think with satisfaction that he had taken not one cent commission for any of his work for the Confederacy (as he claimed was the custom), and that his books had balanced out perfectly when he turned his accounts over to Bulloch on leaving England.

246

He landed at Vera Cruz, Mexico, on May 28, 1865, in the midst of a yellow-fever epidemic.

NOTES TO CHAPTER TWELVE

1. *A New American History*, by Woodward.

2. Letters from Maury to Marin Jansen, December 20, 1862, and April 21, 1863.

3. *Ibid.*

4. The "O. R." is the name generally given to the books published by the government which contain the printed official records of the war. The title of the one from which this information on the cruisers was taken is: *The War of the Rebellion, Records of the Union and Confederate Navies, Series I, Vol. III, Operations of the Cruisers, April 1, 1864–December 30, 1865.*

5. All of these incidents are from the Maury papers at the Library of Congress, his letters, diaries, notes, scrapbook, and those of other members of his family.

6. Letter to his wife, January 23, 1863.

7. Bowling Green is a typical sample of the placid South.

8. Some will try to tell you that Maury designed the *C. S. Ram Stonewall*, but I couldn't find anything to back it up.

9. All this from his letters.

10. Lieutenant Fauntleroy's puerile correspondence is reported at length in the *O. R.*

11. Letter to Jansen, July 23, 1864.

12. All from the *O. R.*

13. Unsigned letter dated March 14, 1865, at Charlottesville, seemingly from Maury's daughter Mary.

14. The *Star* quotes the Liverpool *Post*, April 27, 1865.

15. To "_____ _____, Commanding U. S. Naval Forces in the Gulf of Mexico. At Sea, May 25, 1865. Sir: In peace as in war I follow the fortunes of my native old State

(Virginia). I read in the public prints that she has practically confessed defeat and laid down her arms. In that act mine were grounded also.

"I am here without command, officially alone, and bound on matters of private concern abroad. Nevertheless, and as I consider further resistance worse than useless, I deem it proper formally to so confess, and to pledge you in the words of honor that should I find myself before the final inauguration of peace within the jurisdiction of the United States to consider myself a prisoner of war, bound by the terms and conditions which may have been or may be granted to General Lee and his officers.

"Be pleased to send your answer through my son (Colonel R. L. Maury), a prisoner of war on parole in Richmond.

"In the meantime, and until I hear to the contrary, I shall act as though my surrender had been formally accepted on the above-named terms and conditions. Respectfully, M. F. Maury, Commander, C. S. Navy."

CHAPTER THIRTEEN

Henry and the Splendid Years

JOSEPH HENRY hurried to sound the fire alarm, which telegraphed that a fire was in progress at the Smithsonian to the various government and city fire departments. The box was covered with ice owing to the unusual severity of the recent weather and it took considerable effort to get it open. After joining Mr. Rhees in seeing that their families and everyone else got out of the building, he hustled back to his office to remove his papers, but the fire was raging so furiously, the smoke was so thick, the heat so prostrating, and the sounds of collapsing ceilings so near that he was forced to run for his life. Ten minutes after he had first realized the building was on fire the roof fell in.

The Franklin No. 1 Company, first on the scene, was soon joined by government and other city fire-fighting units. The Provost Guard sent a detail under Lieutenant Patterson to rope off the building and keep the crowds back. Captain

Gilliss arrived from the Observatory as fast as horse and buggy could bring him, and helped Henry, Baird, Rhees, Seaton, others of the staff, firemen, and volunteers in removing museum material and scientific apparatus, and the Henrys' furniture and the contents of the library, while the fire raged through the central portion of the building. Gone was the lecture room and the picture gallery with Stanley's Indian paintings, all the works of art, the offices, the Rhees's apartment, Mr. De Bust's workshop, research laboratories, and storage rooms, all consumed by the flames. *The fire as it mounted the central tower and burst forth in full volume from the main roof, was magnificently grand, and a curious spectacle was presented by the unperturbed steadiness of the revolutions of the anemometer (a wind register) surmounting the tower, while the fierce flame was ravenously mounting to its destruction.* So said the *Star*.[1] Mary Henry, watching, was also impressed, and painfully, by the sight of the anemometer whirling away, more so when the capping and part of the roof of the easternmost of the two central towers collapsed into the flames, while it was almost more than she could bear to see the burning papers that wafted down from her father's office in the main tower.

The firemen confined the flames to the upper floors of the main part of the building, which was their job, but they also took it upon themselves to do some exploring in the remaining rooms. They forced the door to the northeast tower open and poking around in the taxidermist's equipment kept there they found a quantity of whisky. Alas, the brave fire laddies! The whisky was used for preserving specimens and had sulphate of copper dissolved in it. An abstainer ran for Professor Henry and the sufferers were saved by being induced to throw up repeatedly.

Captain Gilliss tried to get the Henrys to move in with them at the Observatory but Henry wouldn't leave the Smithsonian. He and Harriet, up all night, wandered about fearful of the flames breaking out anew, of thefts of their property, of vandalism to the precariously situated remains of the professor's charge, and of the cold weather (down to zero, most rare in Washington) on their guards, now augmented by city policemen. The next day the most important surviving items were safely stowed away. Henry collapsed and was put to bed, suffering from exhaustion and the early symptoms of a cold. A blue sky showed through the empty traceries of the towers and walls upon the cold, wet ruins. The letters, notebooks, and records of scientific experiments covering the last forty years were a charred mass a foot deep in Joseph Henry's office. And there was no insurance on anything. Not that insurance could have brought back the record of a great mind, but that mind could have been practical enough to protect that investment of the Englishman's money of which it was so proud.

The second day after the fire Henry dragged himself off to see the head of the Smithsonian, Abraham Lincoln. He got great sympathy and understanding, and since the yearly meeting of the Board of Regents was just over, the financial situation was clear to both of them. It was decided to rebuild all fireproof, and a temporary roof was ordered built inside the walls so that the regular roof could be built over it. A long discussion was held on how the fire got started, the *Star* having suggested that it might have been incendiary in origin, several thieves having been apprehended in the Smithsonian lately.[2] However Henry explained that the workmen who had been fixing up the picture gallery had put their stovepipe into a faulty flue and that the fire had apparently been smoldering under the roof for several days. Nothing else could have explained the rapidity with which the flames spread.

He got back to the charred shambles of his Norman castle

as a messenger came from the Observatory to say that Captain Gilliss had just dropped dead. Feeling that Gilliss's exertions at the fire might have brought on a heart attack, Henry collapsed a second time. When he heard that the day following the fire Gilliss had had a highly emotional reunion with his son who had just returned from a Confederate prison, he felt less responsible, although still upset about the death of his friend.[3]

With the new roof in place and the weather warmed up, still the Smithsonian building remained so cold that no one could bear to stay in it. Even the ranges, the wings, all crowded with the rescued material and the offices of dispossessed savants, with good heating, were inexplicably cold. Nobody could figure it out. At last the Provost Guard, being fed crackers and hot coffee one night by Mr. De Bust, mentioned that the basement was full of water. After the water was pumped out and two large stoves were installed to get rid of the mustiness, the place was again habitable.[4]

So much had been lost; even the marble copy of the Dying Gladiator crumbled to powder when Mary touched it, having been turned into lime by the heat. Gone besides the priceless Indian paintings were almost all of James Smithson's personal effects, including valuable silver. Joseph Henry's loss was greater than anyone's, but it was not in vain that he was a deacon at the New York Avenue Presbyterian Church. All his religious friends were in a perpetual sweat for fear he would make a public announcement of his belief in Darwin's theories, but he was a better Christian than many of them. His fortitude under his loss was marvelous to behold. He was quite calm, admitting only that it was a blessing that it hadn't happened earlier in his career because he might have found less strength of mind with which to bear it. How he had railed against Faraday's getting the credit for discovering induction! Now, he turned a sincere smile upon the morrow and

252

set to work quite as if he were not sixty-eight years old, with the records of his researches destroyed, his son dead too soon, and the great trust which was his in ruins around him.

This mildness of disposition brought people close to him. Mary wrote in her diary what a blessing they had in their friends.

Elsewhere in Washington and the rest of the Union this was a season of gaiety and triumph. By mid-February the Henrys were back in the swing of things. The Board of Regents met in their dining room to go over Cluss's plan for rebuilding and approve his idea for leaving off the high pointed roof over the easternmost of the two main towers, making it look more like the Abbaye-aux-Dames than the Abbaye-aux-Hommes. It is difficult today to realize that they were making the building plainer, more in the spirit of Romanesque, if never to achieve the virile strength of the true style. The Smithsonian is Gothic in feeling, too refined for the true Romanesque, which has an earthy, brutal power. Probably no one who lived after the twelfth century could build true Romanesque. We can imitate Gothic because it was an art; Romanesque was an experience.

Lincoln's second inaugural was attended by the Henrys in two parts. Joseph went early because he had to sit with the government officials for the swearing in of the vice president and Senate, while Harriet and the girls went later to sit in the gallery and watch. It was so crowded they almost didn't get in and then had to appeal to the doorman, saying they had dismissed their carriage (meaning Tom Datcher had taken the buggy home) and would have to walk home through the mud. Mary was impressed as usual by a scene she felt ought to be impressive, although her description of events followed that in the papers rather too faithfully—everyone looked important and solemn. She recognized Admiral Farragut and General Hooker, and then with lively expectations everyone watched Mr. Andy Johnson sworn in. Mary primly records his speech as radical and like a stump oration. There was a great deal of eyebrow arching, whispers behind hands, and nervous titters from the audience. Then the President, towering over the ushers, moved out to a platform built over the east portico to take his oath before the huge crowd waiting on the Capitol grounds. Mary, who frequently professed her dislike of Lincoln, never saw him without being moved to pity by his expression of sadness and weariness. The members of Congress, the Cabinet, the department heads, the diplomats, and guests got up and followed him out, Mary to watch from a window with Admiral Davis and his two little girls. The crowd was so enormous that Mary was somewhat frightened by it. After the ceremony and Lincoln's short speech were over she still stood there watching. The sun came out very brightly as Lincoln drove away with his son Tad by his side in an open carriage through the ankle-deep mud.

Henry was very interested in the meetings of the Lighthouse Board, since they were starting their most important work on fog-signaling now that the war was nearing a victorious end and they could have the ships necessary for their experiments. He had so many ideas he wanted to try out. He was on the board of visitors of the District of Columbia insane asylum and dutifully inspected the facilities quarterly. He was also working on improving the acoustics of the Capitol and a new ventilation system for it. A heavy windstorm struck the frail remnants of the fire-blasted building and it was seen that the cross walls swayed and would have to come down. A large number of books were received from the French Secretary of the Navy on scientific subjects. The report of the previous year's activities, destroyed in manuscript by the fire, was completed again and submitted to the Regents. Mary went with "a party" to the "front" on an excursion. Mary and her friends saw Fortress Monroe and went without fear of torpedoes up the James to City Point. She regarded the whole affair as "pleasant." It was hardly so to the Confederates who stood about A. P. Hill, dead at Petersburg; even years later, when Lee himself was dying, it was with Hill's name on his lips.

The North felt that the war was all but over when Petersburg fell on April 2, 1865, and Richmond the following day. Guns were firing and church bells were ringing all over town and from the forts around on the hills and over the rivers. The townspeople went on a glorious bender. "Richmond is burning!" they whooped, waving bottles and dancing in the streets. "So let 'er burn!" All the government offices and stores closed, even the observers from the Naval Observatory dropped their reductions of figures placing the stars at such and such a time and joined the hilarious, howling, singing, shouting mob that rallied 'round the flag in Washington that night.

When Lee surrendered at Appomattox on the ninth and Washington woke up to guns announcing it on the tenth, there was a quieter rejoicing. They had relieved their pent-up spirits on the fall of Richmond. The town was illuminated several times in celebration, but the evening of April 13 was set for the "grand" illumination. The Henrys and others at the Smithsonian hurried around putting candles in colored glass shades in rows in every window. That night the building looked in places like a medieval abbey full of defrocked monks who had been at the wine butts and in others like an old ruin lit by ghost lights flickering in the hollow walls. The whole town seemed lighted up, from the white-columned Capitol on its barren hill where the volunteers had cut down the trees for firewood four years before, to the tiniest slum dwelling, all aswim in fire, and the streets a solid mass of people. Watching, wishing she could go out, Mary remembered what she had written in her diary a few days before: *Lee and his whole army are captured. Guns are firing and bells are ring-*

ing out a merry peal. Poor fellows, how hard it must have been to yield. Our hearts are heavy for them even while we rejoice most heartily in the prospects of peace.

The following day Joseph Henry went to New York on business for the Lighthouse Board. He stopped in the lobby of his hotel, the Astor House, to mail a letter late that evening just before he went to bed.

"President Lincoln has been shot and Secretary Seward's throat cut!" a man cried, running in the front door. "It just came in on the telegraph from Washington!"

"Lincoln and Seward? How'd Stanton escape?" said a cool voice near the professor.

"These rumors! I'll never believe another one," said someone else. "Where's the bar?"

Everyone smiled tolerantly, Joseph Henry included. He went on upstairs and to bed.[5]

In the morning it was another story. None of the victims of the weird plot was dead, but neither Lincoln nor Secretary of State Seward's son, stabbed like his father, was expected to live. Slowly, one after another, the church bells began to toll. They wouldn't have bothered for young Frederick Seward; it could mean only one thing.

Joseph Henry sat at the white-and-silver-spread table with his breakfast in his mouth, unable to get it down. All this suffering and doing without, all this long, dreadful war, then to lose the one man they could least afford to lose. Choking, he got up, threw some money on the table, clapped on his tall silk hat, and hurried to get his carpetbag and headed for the station and home. New York was in an ugly mood. Known secesh were hiding after some had been threatened with hanging, and mobs were roaming the streets.

Back in Washington he grabbed the *Evening Star* at the station and hastily read the black-bordered headlines. Booth. *John Wilkes Booth!* He must have been insane. Or, the *Star* suggested, the hireling of Confederate fanatics who had sought by shooting Lincoln in the back at Ford's theater to revenge their losses. The rain-drenched town was already hung with black. Where the bright flags and bunting had been draped to celebrate the victory now hung crape. Silent groups, grim-faced, stood in the rain before shopwindows where the President's picture was displayed in swaths of black. Occasionally came cries and the tramp of hurrying feet as the foolhardy secesh who dared to pull down the black streamers from their own houses were hauled off to jail. "Hang them!" was the cry. With Lincoln dead those who had desired revenge were free to go mad with the getting of it.

Henry sat in the hack silent, riding back to the Smithsonian, listening to the tolling of the bells. He remembered the first time he had seen Lincoln, ill at ease, unkempt, with Seward in the White House. How all his feelings had changed.

Mary ran to meet him, telling how her heart had almost stopped from consternation when she had heard Lincoln had been shot. He had been ungainly and uncouth, but he had been great-hearted and forgiving; and now she could see that he had been truly great.[6]

In their black-hung church Sunday the Lincoln family pew was shut and draped with mourning. The Henrys sat there all through Dr. Gurley's sermon on God's will and looked at that empty pew.

Joseph Henry attended the funeral the following Wednesday. After getting their tickets of admittance at the Treasury he and Professor Baird and Mr. Seaton walked over to the President's House and were ushered into the East Room. A wooden platform in three tiers had been erected around the room, with chairs on it for the dignitaries. Lincoln lay in his long coffin in the center under a black-draped catafalque so high that the central chandelier had been removed to make room for it. The mirrors were covered. The curtains were overdraped with black material. After sermons and prayers by the more important Protestant preachers of the town, Lincoln's own minister, Dr. Gurley of the New York Avenue Presbyterian Church, giving the main sermon, the coffin was closed and carried to the hearse. The dignitaries got gingerly down off the black-hung platform and followed, their carriages being ordered by rank and importance behind the hearse. The representatives of the Smithsonian rode behind the carriages of the assistant department heads and in front of the officers of the Sanitary and Christian Commissions.

In his correspondence Henry noted that the moderates, himself included, mourned for Lincoln but that the radicals said he would have been too lenient with the South and that his death had been all for the good. To Joseph Henry it remained a great calamity, both public and private.[7] On the day of Lincoln's funeral the American flag flew for the first time over the Smithsonian Institution.[8]

The country went into thirty days of mourning and the iron hand of retribution tightened around the South. John Wilkes Booth was shot down in a burning barn in Virginia. Two of the great new monitors built for the Union navy were off Washington in the wide Potomac to intimidate those low or lacking in federal sympathy, since they were regarded as floating fortresses. Many of the Confederate leaders and high-ranking officers were jailed, including General Dabney Herndon Maury. Jefferson Davis was captured and thrown in Fortress Monroe in chains, Ford's Theater was closed "in consequence of the national calamity," and Booth's alleged accomplices were hastily brought to trial. President Johnson was able for the time being to maintain Lincoln's policies of moderation toward the ex-rebels, freely granting amnesties and including under blanket pardons all who took the oath of allegiance except certain groups: those with property

valued at more than twenty thousand dollars, graduates of the
service academies, all those connected with the Confederate
cruisers—in all, some fifteen separate exclusions. This policy
prevailed only until the next session of Congress began and
Thaddeus Stevens and his friends started their program of
vengeance.

Johnson, while a member of Congress before the war, had
once spoken out against the existence of colleges and other
institutions of higher learning as being undemocratic. Henry
had made a point of winning the then senator over to the side
of the desirability of acquiring knowledge at all costs. Now
he went to call on him to present the respects of the Smithsonian Institution staff. He was received cordially, President
Johnson remembering the tall professor well. Johnson, with
his unfortunate inaugural behavior to live down, gave an excellent impression of dignity and modesty.[9] But the vindictive
Yankees were out to get him and he would not be allowed to
live down his emotional outburst at the inauguration.

When the official mourning for Lincoln was over a grand
review of troops was held. Soldiers marched and rode down
Pennsylvania Avenue for two solid days, and nothing more
notable was seen than handsome young General "Custar's"
horse running away with him, to the intense delight of the
crowd. In the bright May sunshine the bands played "The
Battle Hymn of the Republic," "Rally 'Round the Flag,"
"When Johnny Comes Marching Home," the newly composed "Marching Through Georgia," and the never-failing
"The Girl I Left Behind Me"—this last bringing grins and
snickers, since even then they knew the words of a bawdy
version.

The Henrys had eleven house guests to see this parade of
the victorious armies. Mary was exhausted by the first day's
thousands of passing faces but they all had to go back for
more the next day because these were the rough soldiers from

the West. It was like a river of humanity, just like the day before, and terribly oppressive. All the captured battle flags passing, the colorful Zouave uniforms on some of the regiments, the occasional armless sleeve pinned up, the spirited horses, the artillery rumbling along, the faces of the men, everything grew to look alike. It was a great relief to all of them when their day of triumph was over.

Now Washington began to come back down to earth from the wartime tension. Day after day saw the troops depart, some of them pausing for one last long, lingering riot in Swampoodle or Fighting Alley. The hospitals were being evacuated and returned to their original owners or, in the case of the temporary buildings, torn down. Trees were planted around the Capitol and lavish landscaping was begun on the Hill. Negroes continued to flock in, and the Association for the Relief of Destitute Colored Women and Children became a joke, owing to the white directors' imbecilic squabbling. Over on the green slopes of Arlington, where the white tents had once been so thick under the tall columns of the Lee-Custis House, now stood the white stone markers of a new national cemetery. The local constabulary began to make serious raids on the "ranches" and many of the girls left town. The toughs who hung out in the Smithsonian grounds and preyed upon the passers-by were nicknamed the Smithsonian Rangers by the *Star* and were unfailing sources of copy.

Admiral Davis was put in charge of the Naval Observatory to replace the late Captain Gilliss. The Depot of Charts and Instruments was dropped at his request and made a part of the Hydrographic Office. Now Simon Newcomb could truly feel that the Observatory, with its new transit circle made in Germany, was on a par with the great observatories of Europe. The activities were centered on the stars, on the clock that is the stars, and on the maintenance of the ship's instruments as rated by the clock.

A Mexican emigration society was being formed in the North. It got a great deal of publicity, and in no time the *Star* reported 700 men had signed up. The traitor Maury, it was said, was trying to encourage former Confederates to abandon their homes and emigrate to Mexico to join the court of the Emperor. The southern aristocrats were joining Maximilian. The Yankees were for helping the Mexicans. It began to look as if the Civil War would be picked up south of the border.[10]

One of the Confederate cruisers, the commerce destroyer *Shenandoah*, Captain Waddell, C.S.N., was still loose, those on her pretending they didn't know the war was over, destroying Yankee ships, mostly the remnants of the whaling fleet in the North Pacific.[11] Next to the murder of Lincoln, still being blamed on the late government of the South at this period, the most hated act of the Confederacy was the sponsoring of the commerce destroyers. Our shipping industry was dead. Seven hundred of our ships had transferred to foreign registry to protect themselves, and soon Congress would pass a vindictive law refusing those ships permission to be re-registered as American. So we cut off our nose to spite our face. With no expansion possible in trade across the sea our country turned to expansion to the West.

Joseph Henry and his family went to Princeton for graduation in June of 1865. He always responded to the great trees on the campus: how enormous, how green, how calm. . . . From there he went on a month's visit to Lighthouse No. 7, at Bowling Green. He wrote home saying how cool it was there, and reminded them that they had gas at the Smithsonian: there was no need to be using the dangerous new kerosene lamps just because they were fashionable.

261

He went back for the August heat wave, continuing his experiments, working with a magnesium floodlight, and on terrestrial magnetism, his friend Bache's field. Bache was almost daily worse, but Henry kept up his correspondence with him quite as if he were all right. The lighthouses took a great deal of his time now, since so many of them had been damaged or destroyed by rebels during the war. He wrote in his notebook that the New York *Tribune* was the only major paper in the country not to express regret over the fire that had so nearly destroyed the Smithsonian. Work on restoring the building was going forward rapidly, and the fireproof structure reminded him that the rest of the building was not fireproof and that the books really should be disposed of. He finally persuaded the Library of Congress to take them, in 1866.

Under his charge the Smithsonian Institution had become the principal agent of scientific communication in the world. It not only printed technical papers and statistics but sent them free all over the world, and also sent those of other scientific organizations everywhere, and collected those of the world as well. The country's archaeological treasures were noticed and examined and an enlightened public was formed to demand their preservation. A study of the Indians was started, and the Weather Bureau was carried along until a special agency was at last formed under the urging of Professor Cleveland Abbe, and money enough to run the Smithsonian Institution twice over appropriated for it. There was also the correspondence, with scientists needing assistance in their special fields, with people wanting arguments settled. Equipment was located and loaned and struggling scientists encouraged. To show that he was keeping up with the times, when the building was restored the lecture room was not rebuilt, but its space, together with an adjoining laboratory and the art gallery, was made into one large hall. It was used to display Baird's rapidly-growing collection of ethnological treasures. People used to go to the Smithsonian just to see the model of the Indian pueblo Zuñi, which was perfect in every tiny detail.[12]

Henry's persistent contention that the Smithsonian should not be made into a museum continued to be unpopular. An article published in the *Century Magazine* many years later reviewed with pride the growth of the National Museum, originally bequeathed to the Smithsonian's care against Henry's will, and criticized Joseph for his narrow view of the Institution's functions.[13] Well, people might not be satisfied with the amount of room given over to the museum, but anyway no more speeches of which the management did not approve could be made at the Smithsonian!

Almost seventy and destined to live to a ripe old eighty-one, Henry had at last that green old age which the war had threatened so seriously. He did his most important acoustical researches now, and in 1866 the first siren-type fog-signaling device was installed, at the East Beacon on Sandy Hook. Other types were investigated and installed and at last, completely convinced as to its usefulness, he approved kerosene as a fuel for lighthouses.

In early 1867 Alexander Dallas Bache died of the brain tumor that had wasted away his life. He had graduated first in his class at West Point, he had brought the methods of survey measurement to a fine point never seen before, he had been a founder and was first president of the National Academy of Sciences, and he had made notable contributions to the field of education while president of Girard College in Philadelphia. He had persuaded Joseph Henry to share his life of scientific high principles in the Vanity Fair that was Washington. If they together strayed from the path of perfection here, it was from no mean motives, nor for long, but from pure humanly hurt feelings, wronged pride, public embarrassment, and they soon hustled back into their ivory towers with the blessings of all the hardened political sinners around them. Henry wrote in his notebook that he had been closer to Bache—"my respected friend"—than to anyone else except his wife.

And of his wife and family: they were the same. Harriet refused to get old in the Victorian sense of getting fat and wearing a lace cap and *doddering*. Her eyebrows slanted sadly down instead of retaining their youthful arch, her dark hair had some gray in it, but she was fifteen years younger than her husband and she looked it.[14] Their three daughters fussed over them, Mary especially over "Father," but they seem to have been as congenial as families can stay. Joseph Henry's great fondness for reading, for beautiful scenes of nature, for painting, drama, continued through the years. When his secesh friend W. W. Corcoran returned to Washington after the Civil War [15] Joseph Henry was able to get the Regents to allow the Smithsonian art collection that had survived the fire (and people just would give them things) to be transferred to Corcoran's art gallery.

Henry's accessibility was a marvel to everyone. How he could listen with such patience to crackpots and bores and try to point out their errors and not find his attention wandering when a genius showed up shows the habitual sincerity of the man. You might be like John Keely with his engine that ran on half a pint of water and generated enough power to twist iron bars and break cables, and have a line of double talk about hydro-pneumatic-pulsating vacuum machines [16] that lured thousands of dollars out of suckers and yet Joseph Henry wasn't convinced although he listened patiently to Keely's harangues. Or you might be a young teacher of the deaf named Alexander Graham Bell with an idea that in its time sounded as preposterous as the Keely engine, that of transmitting the human voice by wire. But one sentence of

264

Henry and the Splendid Years

Bell's showed Henry that he might have something, out of all the long, confused explanation. In fact, Henry got so enthusiastic that he wanted to go right over to Bell's room and look at the apparatus, although he had a terrible cold and it was raining outside. Bell was so charmed and so encouraged by the white-haired old professor's reaction and by his subsequent interest in his work, that he never failed to give Henry credit for keeping him from giving up. There also came Emile Berliner, whose flat, circular phonograph disc we use today, and whose telephone transmitter surpassed Edison's, which had surpassed Bell's. And from the way Henry urged them to publish and patent their findings we see some gleam of what he might have done could he have lived his life over.

In its issue of January 1872 *Harper's New Monthly Magazine* revealed what happened to Henry's system for ventilating the Capitol. *It is but a step to the Senate chamber, an unimpressive, obscure and unventilated room, which has no contact whatever with the outer air. The desks were removed so that we could observe a system of ventilation which is partly controlled by every Senator. There is an opening like the register of a furnace under each seat, through which fresh air is forced up, and the Senator may either permit it to blow over his august person, which in a hot July evening may be agreeable, or he may close it. But there is a top or cover, which must be turned up or down to open or close the aperture, and it is immovable. To the question what this was meant for, the reply was a benignant smile and the remark that it was designed to prevent Senatorial expectoration into the ventilating tube! For it appears that the fathers of the State are wont to give these conduits of fresh air a quid pro quo; and they had therefore been closed.*

The magazine ran a column of scientific news, "The Editor's Scientific Record." It often featured items about Henry,

265

as this from the issue of August 1874: *In the discovery of new minerals the month has been particularly rich. One, a telluride of lead and iron, he* [Dr. F. M. Endlich of Hayden's Survey] *names Henryite, after Professor Joseph Henry.*

And this, in November 1874: *Langley's observations fully confirm those published in 1845 by Prof. Henry, showing that the solar spots are colder than the adjacent photosphere.* This one also mentions a marker being set up to measure the level of the Great Salt Lake as suggested by Professor Henry.

And this, in January 1875: *Prof. Joseph Henry states that his own observations on the phenomena of sound in connection with fog signals do not confirm the deductions recently made by Prof. Tyndall. The latter attributes the deadening of sounds produced by common fog-bells, the siren, etc., to the reflection and absorption of mixtures of hot and cold air; but Prof. Henry concludes that the loss of sound is due primarily to its refraction, whereby it is bent out of its course to such an extent as to pass over the observer's head.*

And from the column of July 1876: *In connection with the determination of the distance of the sun, the announcement recently made by Prof. Henry that it was proposed to attack this question from the physical side is of importance. The necessary funds for the purpose have been promised, and it is understood that Prof. Newcomb is to undertake a determination of the velocity of light.*

For years Henry's name appeared almost every month, and sometimes two and three times, in the science news. Along with all this, and the vast number of Smithsonian publications, many quoted authoritatively in the above-mentioned column, Henry had time to persuade James Lick to leave the money for the great observatory which bears his name near San Francisco.[17] Only those who understand a character like

266

Lick's, thoroughly misanthropic, can appropriate the magnitude of such a feat.

In 1870 Henry made another trip to Europe, this time accompanied by Mary. While he was there, ostensibly to attend a commission of measures in Paris and to speak on the Smithsonian to the British Parliament's committee on matters of science, he spent a good deal of time sight-seeing in the family-calendar-art areas. Always appreciative of beauty, the sight of the Rhone glacier was a truly memorable experience. He also visited a number of prominent scientists and got involved in the Franco-German War, as an innocent spectator. The following year he took Nell with him to California on a lighthouse-inspection tour. The Chinese theater in San Francisco made more of an impression on him than anything else.

The Centennial Exposition in Philadelphia took a great deal of his time and energy; the Smithsonian had several exhibits there, the ethnological one making the greatest impression. Henry was one of the judges: he accompanied the more important visitors on their rounds, and handed Alexander Graham Bell's embryonic telephone to the Emperor of Brazil with his own hands. Whether Dom Pedro said, "My God! It talks!" or not, the telephone got some gravely needed publicity and Bell was made famous as its inventor. So many of the Centennial's exhibits were given to the Smithsonian that the old Armory, leased with the idea of displaying these objects, proved not large enough to store them packed solidly from floor to ceiling. Professor Baird was obviously going to have to have a building for his National Museum.

The newspapers and magazines then current, the old books, indicate clearly enough that Joseph Henry was *the* scientist of his day. His word was accepted as proof, his hypotheses as valid, in a way that no doubt embarrassed him. In his eightieth year, although few could believe he was that old, a fund was raised to provide him with an additional income, which was to go to his surviving family and after they were all dead, to the National Academy of Science. His friends raised $38,000. He refused at first to accept this proof of national esteem, but was at last persuaded. His wife and dependent children, whom he had not thought to provide for, really didn't need the money, since Harriet was not exactly penniless, but it looked nice.

He went haring off to the Lighthouse Depot at Staten Island in the cold, blustery weather of early December 1877, and one morning woke up with his hand paralyzed. The local doctor thought it was a brain condition, and thoughts of Bache's slow, painful disintegration of faculties gave Henry great concern. It was largely with this in mind that he consented to accept the Joseph Henry fund. His hand improved rapidly, however, and the doctors in Philadelphia pronounced the condition to be nephritis. He went back to Washington sure that since he had never had anything worse than a cold for fifty years that he would last a long time.

Simon Newcomb, now one of the foremost astronomers of the world, was Henry's close friend until the last. He wrote of Henry's last illness: *Beyond a cessation of his active administrative duties there was no change in his daily life. He received his friends, discussed scientific matters, and took the most active interest in the affairs of the world so long as his strength held out. It was a source of great consolation to his family and friends that his intellect was not clouded nor his nervous system shattered by the disease. One of the impressive recollections of the writer's life is that of an interview with him the day before his death, when he was sustained only by the most powerful restoratives. He was at first in a state of slumber, but, on opening his eyes, among the first questions he asked was whether the transit of Mercury had been successfully observed and the appropriation for observing the coming total eclipse secured.*[18]

As he lay dying the following day (May 13, 1878) he spoke in restless slumber of the little *Mistletoe*, the lighthouse tender upon which he had spent so many happy, rewarding hours, and of the wires along which he had sent such fruitful currents. Rousing, he asked those gathered around him to make sure a letter was mailed that he had promised as a courtesy to a stranger, asked what direction the wind was from. . . .

NOTES TO CHAPTER THIRTEEN

1. *Star*, January 24, 1865 (the day of the fire).
2. According to a letter from Henry to Mrs. Bache of April 20, 1866, they stole surgical instruments, chloroform, etc., generally to perform illegal operations.
3. Joseph Henry's journal for 1865.
4. According to Henry's journal the water was discovered February 4, 1865, eleven days after the fire.
5. Letter to Alexander Dallas Bache, April 27, 1865.
6. Mary Henry's diary, April 15, 1865.
7. Letter to his wife, April 21, 1865.
8. Joseph Henry's 1865 notebook.
9. April 27, 1865, letter to Alexander Dallas Bache.
10. *Star*, May 6, 1865, and on.
11. The *Shenandoah* surrendered November 6, 1865.
12. "The Making of a Museum," by E. Ingersoll, in the *Century Magazine*, January 1885.
13. *Ibid.* Note the discrepancies: the Wilkes Exploring Expedition was not "oriental" nor did it go around the world, just for one example.
14. Joseph Henry knocked six years off his age in the 1860 Census.
15. Millionaire Corcoran's attitude toward the war was that he sympathized with the South but could not fight against

the Union: he sat out the war in Europe. This didn't satisfy the government—his house was taken over like Lee's.

16. *Hoaxes*, by MacDougall. Keely was particularly reproachful toward Joseph Henry for not having faith in his invention. After Keely's death the machine was found to have been a hoax, operated by compressed air.

17. Letter from Henry to Professor Huxley, London, August 1, 1874.

18. *Recollections of an Astronomer*, by Newcomb.

CHAPTER FOURTEEN

Maury and the Vox Populi

ONE OF THE amazing things about Mat Maury was his inability, in the spring of 1865, to realize that the people of the South no longer controlled their slaves. His accustomed form of society was gone, his beloved Virginia was a shambles, and in the ruins his peers, suddenly alone, found themselves still able to stand and fight back with an unconquerable spirit if no longer with arms. He thought they must all feel as he did, and it must be remembered that the shocks he suffered had been many and, to one of his easily-stirred emotions, exceedingly severe. *He planned for 200,000 Virginia families to emigrate to Mexico, bringing their slaves to work the fields as bondsmen.* He wrote Captain Jansen on June 8, 1865, of his plan to tell Maximilian of his scheme to bring people "who have had enough of 'vox populi' and are tired of the Republican form of government, and he can call around his throne such an aristocracy as no single monarch ever had the power of establishing within his kingdom."

Taking up quarters in the Hotel Iturbide in Mexico City,

he began to try to sell his electrical-torpedo scheme to General de la Paz, the Minister of War, and at once got over his ears in *mañana*. The *jefe* was all politeness, but he had to think about it. Maximilian and his empress, Carlotta, daughter of the King of Belgium, were at Cuernavaca and Maury had to wait for them to return to the capital. Finally his mail caught up with him and now the full force of his family's disapproval of the Mexican scheme came to his surprised attention. In addition, his friends Jansen, Dr. Tremlett, and Cousin Rutson wrote that he had behaved foolishly. He refused to admit it, and wrote glowing letters of the beauty of the countryside and the delightfulness of the climate, and how all that was needed to make this unfortunate country a paradise was the right kind of people. *His* kind.

Matsy's return on the *Eagle* to New York had been to an enthusiastic welcome from Rutson, alone since his fat sister Ann had hurried South at war's end to look after the nieces and nephews she had raised after her brother William and his wife died. But Rutson, the most sensible of the Maurys and the most moderate, and the one Matsy resembled most in character, realized that there was someone who would want to see Matsy as soon as possible. He got Matsy away to Richmond with some Maury relatives who were traveling that way, and there the boy met his older brother Richard, who went with him to Charlottesville. There Dick hurried on ahead of him to the Refuge (as they called the Infirmary) to tell his mother Matsy would be along shortly. Mrs. Maury was to find the resemblance between Matsy and her lamented Johnny in appearance and behavior quite startling.

There were about twenty-one penniless Maurys at the Refuge.[1] Their discomforts were augmented by worries for Dabney, languishing in Fortress Monroe, where he had been since Lincoln's assassination, and for Mat in Mexico, apparently out of his mind. Richard was still crippled from his war wounds and had taken to drink in a gentlemanly way. Nannie's husband was recovering from nine months in prison at Fort Delaware. Fifteen-year-old Matsy was more interested in shocking people with the electrical machine he had brought from England, although he did write his pa the frankest of letters about how no one took to his Mexico scheme at all.

Maximilian and Carlotta were kindest of the kind to Maury. They gave no serious thought to his emigration scheme, but certainly Maury was regarded as a desirable addition to their court. Captain Chaboone of the French Navy made joking reference to the 200,000—"so many"—and others also, saying he would wreck both Virginia and Mexico. Maury was put in charge of the Mexican National Observatory, to take office as soon as it was built, and was *almost* in charge of emigration, with the title at least of director. He was given a section of land in the new colony, called Carlotta for the empress, near Córdova, and soon moved into a fine house at 13 Calle San Juan Letran.

The war in Mexico (Maury never mentioned in his letters that a revolution was going on all this time) now took such a bad turn for President Juárez, with his troops reduced to 18,000 men under half-a-dozen generals, that his attempt to run out the Imperialistas began to look almost pathetic. The American troops that had been massed on the border in an effort to scare the French away, and had gotten into fist fights with the troops in cantinas around Brownsville, were quietly withdrawn. But the pressure of public opinion in the United States against the French did not abate.

Now that things looked more settled for Maximilian, Dick and Susan began to think more approvingly of the idea of emigrating to Mexico. Mat wangled a job for an assistant at $2,500 (he himself got $5,000) a year out of "Max" and wrote Dick that he could have that. Rutson obligingly sent Dick and Susan and Pip (their infant son) the money to go to Mexico.[2]

Maury, however, without admitting it to anyone else, had his own misgivings about Mexico. He wrote his wife that he would not like to see Tots (his daughter Mary) marry one of these dark-skinned Mexicans, and that he didn't know what to do. Publicly, and even to other members of the family, he was ardently pro-Mexican. He sent Rutson a letter that he asked him to have published in one of the papers in New York, which Rutson refused to handle, saying everyone would think Maury insane if it were published. He *had* to realize slavery was over, no more, vanished. This was in August of 1865: Maury apparently believed the paternalistic pattern of slavery too deeply ingrained to break, that the Negro really could not take care of himself. And that Matthew Fontaine Maury was still doing good in the world. If he could have seen the "free niggers" [3] talking back to his wife mighty snippety and gotten a whiff of the Acquia Creek insurrection then current, where the former slaves were arming to kill off all the white men around and seemed to think they could get away with it, he would have come down to earth in a hurry.

When he finally did understand that Massa and Old Black Joe were no longer bound together legally or otherwise, he insisted that Mrs. Maury and the younger children go to England and meet him there. He wrote that Dick could take over the immigration office (which was going slowly) in Mexico while he was gone. Rutson obliged with passage money and a place for them to stay in England, with his late mother's family, the Bolts, in Birkenhead.

Then, with Mrs. Maury in England, and assured that he would be there in November, Mat abruptly dropped his plans to leave and announced that he would stay in Mexico until spring. He had got what he wanted: the devil with them—or

so it seemed. Richard and Susan were going to the opera almost every night and having a wonderful time, members of
an Emperor's court, more than "gentry." Better to be lords
over the peons in Mexico than be poor and Reconstructed in
Virginia.

The constant reiteration of the French was that the only
thing wrong with Mexico was the Mexicans. The *hacendados*,
the wealthy landowners, were their especial abomination.
The peons they found lovable, stupid, apparently docile to
their domination. They wanted the southern aristocracy to
replace the *hacendados*.[4] They would know how to handle the
peons without undue cruelty and they would bask apprecia-
tively in the smiles of the French emperor. Maximilian's idea
of improving Mexico was to build an opera house. Handsome,
blond, as fond of solitude as an alcoholic of gin, he was capable
of believing himself the benefactor of a trouble-stirred country. Carlotta, mad for crown and regalia, was more practical.
Between them and their French generals, and the slippery-
minded Napoleon III over the sea, nothing came of their reign
but more trouble for Mexico. And they loved the country, so
sunny, so colorful, and complained that they were not everywhere welcomed with open arms.

Maury wrote a short biography of Monseigneur de Lambastida, which was translated into Spanish with other sketches
by Ángel Pola in Mexico City in 1900, under the title: *Los
Traidores pintados por el mismo* (*The Traitors as Painted
by Themselves*). Pelagio de Lambastida was the once-ban-
ished archbishop of Mexico, whose return to power by the
French was one of their excuses for invading Mexico (it was
for the good of the Church), and which was mutually regretted.

Maury now proceeded to take out Mexican naturalization
papers,[5] for which he was royally castigated in the American
press, so he could get his first quarter's pay.[6] As soon as he

got his money he began to make broad hints to the Empress that it would be necessary for him to take a trip in the early spring to visit his family in England.

Maury apparently was playing both ends against the middle: old, alone, frightened for himself and desperate for his family, he wanted to be a big noise in the court of the Emperor of Mexico—but if that court failed, he wanted to have a safe place to retreat to. He wanted his family out of the States because he was afraid they would be punished for his defection. Dabney had been released from Fortress Monroe and William L. Maury, late captain of the Confederate commerce destroyer *Georgia*, walked the streets of Richmond a free man. Even the guerrilla raider Mosby had given himself up with no fear. But Jeff Davis was still in Fortress Monroe, Wirz of Andersonville was sure to hang, and there was talk of further retribution. That Thaddeus Stevens and his friends knew of subtler but more effective punishments didn't occur to him. Maury just wasn't taking any chances.

The last of November the fearful shell of his worries cracked a little and he wrote his wife a letter almost realistic in his acceptance of the situation. He wanted her away from the discomforts of Reconstruction but he knew that she wouldn't like Mexico. So he would come to see her in England as soon as he could. *He might not go back to Mexico but she was to tell no one.* He added testily that he hated having to explain. Then he calmly went on to say Dick was doing wonderfully, and again he raved about the beauties of Mexico and asserted that thousands were longing to move there. Poor Mrs. Maury; it was, no doubt, a good thing she was much given to praying.[7]

By January 1866 Maury realized that all was up with him in Mexico. Despite his fancy title he had never been given complete charge of immigration [8] and few people took advantage of his plan. His own newspaper, one he had written

276

so much for that he felt it was his own, the Richmond *Whig*, attacked him and his emigration scheme, saying that if Lee and others like him could stand Virginia in defeat that the rest of them could, too, and took violent exception to Maury's use of the word "gentry." Virginia's "gentry" these days were hoeing their own corn and chopping their own wood and hauling their own water, and knew their days as lords of the manor were over. Maury, if a little cracked, was not stupid. Maximilian's hold on his throne had grown very unsteady after a brief period of triumph. Juárez was a dedicated and determined patriot, Mexico was his life, his very soul. Maury was capable of a dignified retreat but now he hid his intentions. The Empress gave him a leave of absence approved by "Maximiliano." Maury left his son and daughter-in-law and grandson as proof that he was only going on a journey. A man of his honor would not abandon them in a country he considered dangerous. Everyone knew that.

When Maury got to Vera Cruz on March 8, 1866, ready to board a French ship bound for St. Nazaire, he found his salary had been stopped—dear me. He missed the boat, but Maximilian gave him an appointment as being on imperial business,[9] and with matters now clearly understood, the honorable imperial agent set out for England on the next boat, the British mail steamer *Conway*. He arrived in Liverpool on March 29, 1966. Two weeks later the Emperor wrote him a polite letter of dismissal.

It had turned out, all in all, not too badly. He still dwelt on the beauties of Mexico and swore his scheme would have worked if only everybody else had supported it. But "Max" was too good for the likes of the Mexicans, he explained. His family and friends in the States kept writing him: *Don't come home. You'll be arrested.*

To his family in England his appearance was as great a shock as his recent behavior had been. His beard was white and what was left of his hair was nearly so. His expression was habitually downcast, sad-looking; his spirit seemed broken. No more did the little jokes intersperse his conversation. He was glum, almost grim. How they would have loved to have heard even the most feeble of his jokes, remembering perhaps: "When is a sick man like one who mistreats his wife? When he takes an e-lix-ir." [10] He was desperate for something to do and badly in need of money. He considered himself *the* authority on the subject of mines, and proposed to teach it to the war offices of nations for a stiff fee, $2,500 a country. Moving from their house on Cavendish Square to lodgings on the outskirts of London at 41 Clarendon Terrace, Belsize Road, he set up his course of instruction on both land mines and underwater mines.

His first students were representatives of Norway and Sweden, then came those of Holland. He taught the French in France, startling the Emperor by blowing up the Seine as lustily as he had once blown up the James, and received a flattering offer of French citizenship. His homesick family was supposed to have prevailed on him to refuse it, but on July 8, 1866, he wrote Rutson wistfully that he had heard no more about turning Frenchman, so apparently Napoleon III was big on talk and short on action with others besides Maximilian. In his school Maury played no favorites, offering his services both to the King of Württemberg and to the King of Prussia, who were having a difference of opinion at the time. He even offered his services to Canada, no doubt thinking joyfully of the Canadian-American border lined with land mines and the Great Lakes a-bob with floating mines.

His friend Reverend Tremlett had been busy for several years trying to raise a Maury Fund, with many a setback as the slavery question became more and more of an abomination to more and more of the British. But at last he was able to

278

enlist the good feelings of some British naval officers and
scientists, some of the upper crust who believed there should
be sharp divisions of society, and the heads of some foreign
governments who felt they owed Maury something in return
for his Wind and Current Charts. No one in the United States
could be persuaded to donate except Rutson, who no doubt
contributed a large amount, since Tremlett wrote Maury
about this time that he had no truer friend than Rutson,
even if he did think there was no country like the United
States and such "bosh." They were able to raise the sum of
3,000 guineas (a little more than fifteen thousand dollars),
which was packaged up in a silver-gilt casket and presented
to Maury at a testimonial dinner held at Willis's Room in
London on June 5, 1866. The Netherlands, no doubt after
earnest appeals by Jansen, had given £1,100, the Grand
Duke Constantine a thousand, and the rest was donated by
Rutson and others. The dinner was attended by such important people as the First Lord of the Admiralty, the Mexican Ambassador, and the John Laird who had built the
Alabama and the *Florida.*

Some seeds of the cinchona (the tree whose bark produces
quinine), which Maury had ordered, finally arrived and he
forwarded them to Maximilian, settling his accounts with
Mexico forever. Dick had just written that he had been replaced in the immigration office, and the Liberals had occupied his plantation ("it's not worth anything anyway" [11]),
and he had been lucky to find a job with a British company for
a couple of weeks to keep from starving. His father obligingly
went out and begged a job for him, as assistant manager of
a mine at Javali, Nicaragua, which was owned by a British
company. Dick could not go back to Virginia because Secretary of State Seward had made him take an oath never to
return to the United States when he emigrated to Mexico.

Maury's family in England at this time included Mrs.

Maury, Matsy, who was attending the Royal School of
Chemistry, and his youngest daughters, Eliza, Mary, and
Lucy. They had become great friends of the Tremletts and
others with whom they visited around, but they were always
homesick for Virginia and their relatives and friends there,
their "charming circle," as they thought of it. But there was
no understanding Pa these days. One had to be patient.

Cyrus Field was determined to lay the Atlantic cable and
with the war out of the way he was able to get support and
material enough to let him tackle the job with his usual
energy. This time no one paid any attention to Maury, although all the preparations were made in England. The first
postwar attempt failed in the summer of 1865. When the
Great Eastern was chartered and Professor William Thom-
son was induced to do the electrical work and elaborate plans
were made for another attempt in the summer of 1866, Maury
wrote his Dutch oceanographer friend Jansen that nothing
would come of it.[12] However, this time they laid a successful
cable and went back and fished up the end of the previous
summer's lost cable, spliced onto it, and ran back to their
base at Heart's Content, Newfoundland, with two good working cables connecting the continents. Anyone who wanted to
use it (they stood in line) was welcome to, at a dollar a letter.[13]
Only Maximilian connected Maury with the successful laying of the Atlantic cable and sent him a medal. Despite the
tone of his letters to Jansen, Maury had been working on
plans for a cable with the British electrical company that had
contracted to handle his mines, inventing devices for laying
the cable and covering it, but nothing came of it.

Fortunately the Richardson Publishing Company in New
York asked Maury to write some geography textbooks for
younger children and so the pen saved him again. He wrote
and wrote for two years, to Mrs. Maury's great relief. They
made a family project of it, discussing the work freely as he

dictated it to his daughters, and Matsy made all the maps, and it helped the time go by. The summer of 1867, Maury's second oldest daughter, Nannie Corbin (she who had defied the Yankee soldiers so spiritedly at Charlottesville) arrived in London to stay with her mother while she had her second child. Her home at Farley Vale had burned and her husband was almost penniless, which had something to do with it, too. The child was named John Herndon Maury Corbin, and Mat became very fond of him.

At last Mat was able to make a decision that had been bothering him for a long time. Although he was intensely religious, and felt close to silent Big Nannie because she spent so much time on her knees, he had never joined a church. After many long talks with Dr. Tremlett he at last decided to join the Episcopal Church. In Tremlett's Anglican church in Belsize Park, Maury was confirmed by Dr. Quintard, the Bishop of Tennessee, who had come to England to raise money for the Episcopalian-sponsored University of the South, at Sewanee. Joining with him were Matsy and Lucy. Big Nannie, an Episcopalian herself, could see some of her prayers answered.

Three years of exile were drawing to a close. Maximilian had been executed by a Mexican Nationalista firing squad in June of 1867, and had died as nobly and as stupidly as he had lived. Carlotta was insane and under protective custody at a country villa in Belgium. A few former Confederates had successfully emigrated to Mexico and other countries but the overwhelming majority were sticking it out at home.

Cambridge University, disregarding the fact that the United States was insisting that England pay for the ships and cargoes destroyed by the Confederate commerce raiders and thus admit to a fault,[14] honored Maury with an LL.D at their exercises in June of 1868, with Queen Victoria unveiling a statue of the late Prince Consort there. In red robes,

Maury heard himself praised in Latin for his contributions to the science of oceanography and his noble self-sacrifice during the recent war.

At last it became clear that he would be able to go home safely. Only Jefferson Davis was still beyond the pale, and Horace Greeley (to the ruination of his political hopes, as it turned out) had gotten him released on bail. No one mentioned that Maury had become a citizen of Maximilian's dead Mexican empire. No one wanted to remember it. There would be no brass bands playing at the pier to meet him but no one would rotten-egg him or serve him with subpoenas, either. Of several job offers he accepted the one that seemed to ask the least of him, doing some statistical work for Virginia Military Institute.

And so, with all his family except Matsy, who was left studying mining engineering in England, he arrived in New York on July 16, 1868. It was a very hot day and Maury was overcome, he said, by the heat.[15] They had to call a doctor to attend to him. Everyone was very kind and it was more than he could stand, to come home, and feel that it was home, and that he was welcome. He saw that the Yankees he had dreaded facing were solicitous and he was deeply touched. The little, limping, white-haired old man with the large proud name so lately tagged with the epithet "traitor" was an American among Americans again. He stood in the shelter of that *vox populi* which he had cursed, and was glad that it existed.

After taking care of some publishing matters and trying to express his gratitude to that gruff good angel Rutson, he followed his family to Richmond. He had to go through Washington to get there, but whether with loathing or longing for the copper dome with its telescope slit by the Potomac where he had been so happy and successful, he made no comment. Richmond was another story: shocked, he saw the shabby South for the first time, idle Negroes lounging on the streets, respectable white people wearing rags and sporting calluses, the neat houses scarred and bedraggled, the fields ill tended, the capital only now beginning to recover from its siege and burning, everything poverty-stricken. But there was nothing skimped or scanty in the warmth of his welcome. He was a great man of the South, Commodore Maury, the "Pathfinder of the Seas."

For the next four and a half years he had a measure of the honorable condition due his contributions to man's welfare. He was not required to carry a regular teaching load at V.M.I., but on occasion gave talks to the students on general subjects. His prime work was the compiling of records on the natural resources of Virginia and making a general physical survey of the state. He also wrote more textbooks for children and traveled around making speeches on the glorious future of the South that were pleasant to listen to. He had the usual upsets and thwarted plans which were a by-product of being himself. The situation at V.M.I. was in the nature of a sine-cure, which he felt was due him most of the time. The house they furnished him was castellated in true military fashion (if one's ideas of such coincides with Sir Walter Scott's), and in its beautiful setting looked like a miniature medieval castle.

It was all very pleasant, but the fire that had been fed by ambition and pride was out. Like many another, he had been destroyed by the war. At last he could drag himself limping around no longer.

"My dear, I have come home to die," he said to Big Nannie, coming home from making a speech in Norfolk in October of 1872. Most of his family was there; the government had relented and let Dick back in the country, but no one could change his mind. He meant it, dramatics or no: he went to bed and gave up.

Perhaps in the sleepless nights, painfully tossing, he saw

again in memory the beautiful stars that form Theta Orionis, one white, one lilac, one garnet, one red, with the equatorial at the Observatory, or saw the precise arrival of the vernal equinox through the little transit instrument. Perhaps he saw the deep-blue waters of the southern part of the Gulf Stream, sharply divided from the gray-green ocean waters. Or the palm-shaded beach by Comptroller Bay on Nukahiva. Or traced again the winds and currents of the ocean that he had loved less than this Virginia where he died on February 1, 1873. He sent Big Nannie and his daughters and grandchildren out of the room (spunky Nannie Corbin hid behind the head of the bed).[16] To his sons and sons-in-law he spoke briefly of how he felt, and then at last he could say, all is well.

NOTES TO CHAPTER FOURTEEN

1. *Matthew Fontaine Maury, U.S.N. and C.S.N.*, by Corbin.

2. This after Dick had sent him an I-hate-all-Yankees letter, in which he grudgingly thanked Rutson for helping them with money earlier, because he felt when he owed a debt he should say thank you, even to a Yankee.

3. The word "nigger" was not used in any of the Maury correspondence until after the war. They were "servants." Matsy wrote his pa that summer (1865) that his mother was about ready to go to Mexico to get away from the "free nigger" servants, and that they'd had three cooks since he'd been home.

4. *Juárez and His Mexico*, by Roeder, quoting an unnamed French officer.

5. Rutson to Tremlett, October 13, 1865. Says pointblank Maury is no longer a citizen of the United States.

6. From his letters it is not clear whether this pay was

for his job as Director of Immigration or as Director of the unbuilt Observatory.

7. In his will Maury commented on the good example her piety had always set him.

8. Letter to Mrs. Maury, September 23, 1865; to Corbin October 31, 1865.

9. Rutson to Hasbrouck, March 15, 1866.

10. To William Blackford, March 12, 1849.

11. To Hasbrouck, July 28, 1866. Córdoba is in the heart of one of the richest, most beautiful agricultural areas you'd ever want to see.

12. May 2, 1866.

13. A letter-of-the-alphabet understood. *Adventures in America*, by Kouwenhoven.

14. These claims were decided in August of 1872, after considerable stubborn litigation, the British paying the Americans fifteen and a half million dollars as a result.

15. Letter to Jansen, July 17, 1868.

16. *Matthew Fontaine Maury, U.S.N. and C.S.N.*, by Corbin.

CHAPTER FIFTEEN

And So Then—

AMERICA'S GREAT upheaval had turned the paths trod by Joseph Henry and Matthew Fontaine Maury. But, much as the lives of these two were influenced by their great decision, and crushing as the circumstances of the war proved, still those lives had been cast in a certain vein long before the war. Maury likely would have been denounced as a fraud sooner or later, even without the impetus of the "traitor" situation. Henry, without the distractions of war, would have gone on with his plans for the Weather Bureau, and perhaps all the circumstances of that pet peeve of his would have been quite different today, if Maury had stayed in the field to annoy him. Possibly these two would have destroyed each other as scientists by their childish rancour.

But that war, which changed their lives, also changed the national attitude toward science. After the war came schools to teach engineering, the bridge between pure and practical science. Mathematics began its snowballing command over the scientific world, both in discovery and application. And those who had done their work outside the framework of mathematics were forgotten.

Such relics of a physical nature as Maury and Henry left behind you may see for yourself in the glass-shielded cases of the Smithsonian Institution: Henry's first electromagnet, Maury's enormous collection of foreign orders and medals, some of them diamond-studded, the ornate silver service presented to him by the New York shipping interests, even the red robe he wore when he got his honorary degree from Cambridge. There are lengths of the Atlantic cable there, and telegraph machines of strange appearance, and, stored away, the first weather map.

In front of the old building at the Smithsonian, now grown to many buildings in every field from astrophysical observatories to zoos, Joseph Henry stands in bronze, and also before the former Albany Academy. The Maury memorial on Monument Avenue in Richmond has him in bronze, seated below a globe, with a chart across his lap. Joseph Henry lies buried in Oak Hill Cemetery in Washington in quiet simplicity. Maury lies grandly between two presidents, surrounded by the heroes of the Confederacy, in Hollywood Cemetery in Richmond.

Bibliography

Appleton's Cyclopedia of American Biography, New York, 1900.

Astronomical and Meteorological Observations Made at the United States Naval Observatory During the Year 1867, Washington, 1870.

Bell, John. "Speech of Hon. John Bell, of Tennessee, on the Naval Retiring Board, delivered in the Senate of the United States, April 28 and 29, 1856," Washington, 1856.

Bernhard, Hubert J., Bennett, Dorothy A., Rice, Hugh S. *New Handbook of the Heavens*, New York, 1954.

Bill, Alfred Hoyt. *The Beleaguered City, Richmond, 1861–1865*, New York, 1946.

Billington, Ray Allen. "The Know-Nothing Uproar," *American Heritage*, February 1959.

Bowditch, Nathaniel (originator). *American Practical Navigator, An Epitome of Navigation*, Washington (no year).

Braynard, Frank O. *Famous American Ships*, New York, 1956.

Brock, R. A. *Documents, Chiefly Unpublished, Relating to the Huguenot Emigration to Virginia and to the Settlement at Manakin-Town*, Virginia Historical Society, Richmond, 1886.

Brockett, L. P., and Vaughn, Mary. *Woman's Work in the Civil War*, Philadelphia, 1867.

Brooks, Van Wyck. *The World of Washington Irving*, New York, 1944.

Bruce, Robert V. *Lincoln and the Tools of War*, Indianapolis, 1956.

Buchanan, Lamont. *Ships of Steam*, New York, 1956.

Butterfield, Roger. *The American Past, A History of the United States from Concord to Hiroshima, 1775–1945*, New York, 1947.

Butts, Francis. "The Loss of the Monitor, by a Survivor," *Century Magazine*, December 1885.

Carnegie, Andrew. *Autobiography*, New York, 1920.

Carse, Robert. *Blockade, the Civil War at Sea*, New York, 1958.

Carson, Rachel L. *The Sea Around Us*, New York, 1951.

Catton, Bruce. *This Hallowed Ground*, New York, 1956.

Chapin, Henry and Smith, F. G. Walton. *The Ocean River*, New York, 1952.

Chesnut, Mary Boykin. *A Diary from Dixie*, Boston, 1949.

Childe, Professor V. Gordon. *Man Makes Himself*, New York, 1951.

Clark, George R., Stevens, William O., Alden, Carroll S., and Krafft, Herman F. *A Short History of the United States Navy*, Philadelphia, 1920.

Clarke, Arthur C. *Voice Across the Sea*, New York, 1958.

Cockran, Hamilton. *Blockade Runners of the Confederacy*, Indianapolis, 1958.

Colston, R. E. "Watching the Merrimac," *Century Magazine*, March 1885.

Corbin, Diana Fontaine Maury. *Matthew Fontaine Maury, U.S.N. and C.S.N.*, London, 1888.

Coulson, Thomas. *Joseph Henry, His Life and Works*, Princeton, 1950.

Cowles, Captain Calvin D. *Atlas to Accompany the Official*

Records of the Union and Confederate Armies, Washington, 1891–95.

Craven, Avery O. *Civil War in the Making*, Baton Rouge, 1959.

Crozier, William Armstrong (ed.). *Spotsylvania County Records, 1721–1800*, Richmond, 1955.

Current, Richard. *The Lincoln Nobody Knows*, New York, 1958.

Davis, Varina Howell. *Jefferson Davis, Ex-President of the Confederate States*, New York, 1890.

de Terra, Helmut. *Humboldt*, New York, 1955.

Dictionary of American Biography, New York, 1936.

Dodds, John W. *The Age of Paradox, a Biography of England, 1841–1851*, New York, 1952.

Dreppard, Carl. *Pioneer America, Its First Three Centuries*, New York, 1949.

Dugan, James. *The Great Iron Ship*, New York, 1953.

Durant, John and Alice. *Pictorial History of American Ships on the High Seas and Inland Waters*, New York, 1953.

Eiseley, Loren. "Charles Lyell," *The Scientific American*, August 1959.

Eisenschiml, Otto, and Newman, Ralph. *The Civil War: The American Iliad*, New York, 1956.

Encyclopedia Americana, New York, 1953.

Eskew, Garnett Laidlaw. *A Pageant of the Packets, A Book of American Steamboats*, New York, 1929.

Forester, C. S. *The Age of Fighting Sail*, Garden City, New York, 1956.

Freuchen, Peter. *Peter Freuchen's Book of the Seven Seas*, New York, 1957.

Furnas, J. C. "Patrolling the Middle Passage," *American Heritage*, October 1958.

Gill, Theo. "The First Century of the Republic: Scientific Progress," *Harper's Monthly*, January 1876.

Goode, George Brown. *An Account of the Smithsonian Institution, Its Origin and History, Objects and Achievements*, Washington, 1895.

291

————. *The Smithsonian Institution, the History of Its First Half Century*, Washington, 1897.

Goss, Warren Lee. "Recollections of a Private: Up the Peninsula with McClellan," *Century Magazine*, March 1885.

Graves, Robert. "Minorca," *Holiday*, January 1960.

Gray, Jane Loring (ed.). *Letters of Asa Gray*, New York, 1893.

Greene, Commander S. Dana. "In the 'Monitor' Turret," *Century Magazine*, March 1885.

"Growth of Our Theories of the Weather," *Harper's Monthly*, January 1872.

Harrison, C. C. "A Virginia Girl in the First Year of the War," *Century Magazine*, August 1885.

Hassler, Warren W., Jr. *General George B. McClellan, Shield of the Union*, Baton Rouge, 1957.

Hay, John. *Lincoln and the Civil War as Seen in the Diaries and Letters of John Hay*, New York, 1939.

Hendrick, Burton J. *Statesmen of the Lost Cause*, New York, 1939.

Henry, Joseph. *Collected Works of Joseph Henry*, Washington, 1889.

————. *Scientific Writings of Joseph Henry*, Washington, 1887.

————. Letters, journals, personal papers in ms.

Henry, Joseph, A Memorial, printed by order of Congress, 1880.

Henry, Mary. Diary, 1861–65 in ms.

Henry, Robert Selph. *The Story of the Confederacy*, New York, 1943.

Hogan, Donald W. "Unwanted Treasures of the Patent Office," *American Heritage*, February 1958.

Horan, James D. *Mathew Brady, Historian with a Camera*, New York, 1955.

Ingersoll, Ernest. "The Making of a Museum," *Century Magazine*, January 1885.

Instruments and Publications of the United States Naval Observatory, Washington, 1845–1876, Washington (no date).

Jackson, Frederick Turner. *The Frontier in American History*, New York, 1920.

Jaffe, Bernard. *Men of Science in America*, New York, 1958.

Jordan, E. L. (ed.). *Hammond's Nature Encyclopedia of America*, New York, 1955.

Kean, Robert Garlick Hill. *Inside the Confederate Government*, New York, 1957.

Kimmel, Stanley. *Mr. Lincoln's Washington*, New York, 1957.

Knox, Dudley W. *A History of the United States Navy*, New York, 1936.

Kouwenhoven, John A. *Adventures in America, 1857–1900*, New York, 1938.

Lane, Ferdinand. *The Mysterious Sea*, New York, 1947.

Leech, Margaret. *Reveille in Washington, 1860–1865*, New York, 1941.

Leslie, Frank. *Historical Register of the United States Centennial Exhibition, 1876*, New York, 1877.

Lewis, Charles Lee. *Matthew Fontaine Maury, Pathfinder of the Seas*, Annapolis, 1927.

Liep, Hans. *River in the Sea*, New York, 1957.

Lives in Science, New York, 1957.

Lorant, Stefan. *Lincoln, A Picture History of His Life*, New York, 1952.

Mabee, Carleton. *The American Leonardo, Samuel F. B. Morse*, New York, 1943.

MacDougall, Curtis D. *Hoaxes*, New York, 1958.

Mack, Edward C. *Peter Cooper, Citizen of New York*, New York, 1949.

MacKenzie, Catherine. *Alexander Graham Bell*, New York, 1928.

Maury, Anne Fontaine (ed.). *Intimate Virginiana, A Century of Maury Travels by Land and Sea*, Richmond, 1941.

Maury, Dabney Herndon. *Recollections of a Virginian*, New York, 1894.

Maury, Matthew Fontaine. *Explanations and Sailing Directions to Accompany Wind and Current Charts*, Washington, 1858.

293

————. *The Physical Geography of the Sea*, New York, 1856.

————. Letters and other ms.

Maury, Richard L. *A Brief Sketch of the Work of Matthew Fontaine Maury During the War 1861–65*, Richmond, 1915.

Maxwell, William Quentin. *Lincoln's Fifth Wheel*, New York, 1956.

Melville, Herman. *Typee*, New York (reprinted), 1958.

————. *White Jacket*, New York, 1850.

Merrill, James M. *The Rebel Shore*, Boston, 1957.

Metgang, Herbert (ed.). *Lincoln as They Saw Him*, New York, 1956.

Milhollen, Hirst D., and Kaplan, Milton. *Divided We Fought*, New York, 1952.

Morgan, James Morris. *Recollections of a Rebel Reefer*, New York, 1917.

Morris, Richard B. (ed.). *Encylopedia of American History*, New York, 1953.

National Cyclopedia of American Biography, New York, 1899.

Nevins, Allan. *The War for the Union, Vol. I, The Improvised War*, New York, 1959.

"New Washington," *Harper's Monthly*, February, 1875.

Newcomb, Simon. *Reminiscences of an Astronomer*, New York, 1903.

Newman, Ralph, and Long, E. B. *The Civil War, the Picture Chronicle*, New York, 1956.

Odgers, Merle M. *Alexander Dallas Bache, Scientist and Educator*, Philadelphia, 1947.

Outhwaite, Leonard. *The Atlantic, A History of an Ocean*, New York, 1957.

Parker, Amasa (ed.). *Landmarks of Albany County, New York*, Syracuse, 1897.

Pendray, B. Edward. *Men, Mirrors and Stars*, New York, 1946.

Photographic History of the Civil War, 10 vols., New York, 1957.

Pratt, Fletcher. *Civil War in Pictures*, Garden City, New York, 1955.

————. *A Compact History of the United States Navy*, New York, 1957.

————. *Ordeal by Fire*, New York, 1948.

Rhees, William J. *The Smithsonian Institution and National Museum*, Philadelphia, 1869.

Robinson, John, and Dow, George Francis. *The Sailing Ships of New England*, Westminster, Maryland, 1953.

Roeder, Ralph. *Juárez and His Mexico*, New York, 1947.

Roosevelt, Theodore. *The Naval War of 1812*, New York, 1882.

Roscoe, Theodore, and Freeman, Fred. *Picture History of the U. S. Navy, from Old Navy to New, 1776 to 1897*, New York, 1956.

Sandburg, Carl. *Abraham Lincoln: the War Years*, New York, 1939.

Sands, Rear Admiral B. F. *Astronomical and Meteorological Observations Made During the Year 1871 at the United States Naval Observatory*, Washington (no date).

Sleeman, Charles. *Torpedoes and Torpedo Warfare*, Portsmouth, 1889.

Soley, James Russell. *The Sailor Boys of '61*, Boston, 1888.

Somervell, D. C. *English Thought in the Nineteenth Century*, New York, 1936.

Spears, John R. *The History of Our Navy*, New York, 1897.

Stern, Philip Van Doren (ed.). *The Life and Writings of Abraham Lincoln*, New York, 1940.

Swanberg, W. A. *First Blood, the Story of Fort Sumter*, New York, 1957.

Taylor, Richard. *Destruction and Reconstruction, Personal Experiences of the Late War*, New York, 1955.

Throm, Edward L. *Picture History of American Transportation*, New York, 1952.

Tout, T. F. *An Advanced History of Great Britain*, New York, 1910.

Trevelyan, George McCauley. *British History in the Nineteenth Century*, New York, 1939.

True, Webster Prentice. *The Smithsonian, America's Treasure House*, New York, 1950.

Tryon, Warren S. (ed.). *A Mirror for Americans*, Chicago, 1952.

Tunis, Edward. *Oars, Sails and Steam, A Picture Book of Ships*, New York, 1952.

Upton, Monroe. *Electronics for Everyone*, New York, 1957.

Vanderbilt, Cornelius, Jr. *The Living Past of America*, New York, 1955.

Virginia Magazine of History and Biography, Vol. 10, 1903.

Waite, Edward. *The Washington Directory and Congressional and Executive Directory for 1850*, Washington, 1850.

War of the Rebellion: Records of the Union and Confederate Navies, Series I, Vol. III, Washington, 1896.

Wayland, John W. *The Pathfinder of the Seas, the Life of Matthew Fontaine Maury*, Richmond, 1930.

Weber, Gustavus A. *The Naval Observatory, Its History, Activities and Organization*, Baltimore, 1926.

————. *The Weather Bureau, Its History, Activities and Organization*, New York, 1922.

Weiss, George. *The Lighthouse Service*, Baltimore, 1926.

West, Richard S. Jr. *Mr. Lincoln's Navy*, New York, 1957.

Whitridge, Arnold. "The Peaceable Ambassadors," *American Heritage*, April, 1957.

Wilkes, Charles. *Narrative of the United States Exploring Expedition During the Years 1838–1842*, Philadelphia, 1844.

Wilson, Mitchell. *American Science and Invention*, New York, 1954.

Woodward, W. E. *A New American History*, New York, 1937.

WPA. *New York, A Guide to the Empire State*, New York, 1940.

————. *Tennessee, A Guide to the State*, New York, 1939.

————. *Virginia, A Guide to the Old Dominion*, New York, 1940.

Periodicals:

Washington *Daily Star* and *Evening Star*, 1854–66.

Century Magazine, November 1884 to September 1886.

Harper's Monthly, incomplete collection, 1857 to 1884.

Scientific American, January to June 1862.

Index

297

Fredericksburg, Virginia, 11-12, 49, 101, 188, 198, 202-203
Fredericksburg, Battle of, 210

Gale, Prof. Leonard, 78, 84, 128
Galway, New York, 29, 30, 64, 72
Georgia, C.S.S., 216, 235, 239
Gettysburg, Battle of, 218
Gilliss, Capt. James, 95, 97, 100, 111 *foot.*, 159, 168, 169, 170, 249-250, 252
Glynn, Lt. James, 54, 55
Goldborough, Adm. L. M., 95, 225
Gosport Navy Yard (Norfolk), 148, 176, 188, 193, 200
Grant, Gen. Ulysses S., 179, 197, 218, 222, 223, 224, 237
Gray, Prof. Asa, 8, 86 *foot.*, 139
Great Circle sailing, 57
Great Britain, 13, 88
Greeley, Horace, 132, 134, 145, 146, 155, 158, 165, 174-175, 282
Gunboats, 19, 193, 194, 196
Guyot, Arnold, 121, 209

Hampton Roads, 13, 54, 176, 197, 199, 244
Harper's Ferry, 137, 148
Harpeth Academy, 22, 24
Harrison's Landing, 180, 200, 207
"Harry Bluff, U.S.N." *See* Maury, Cmdr. Matthew Fontaine.
Hasbrouck, William, 24, 192, 202, 237
Hendrie family. *See* Henry.
Henry, the; international unit of self-induction, 8
Henry, Ann Alexander, 27, 28, 34, 36

Henry, Caroline ("Carrie"), 83, 154, 183, 209, 220
Henry, Harriet Alexander (Mrs. Joseph Henry), 66, 67, 73, 75, 76, 83, 86 *foot.*, 126, 154, 181, 182, 183, 216, 220, 224, 228, 251, 253, 264, 268
Henry, Helen ("Nell"), 83, 154, 183, 219, 267
Henry, James, 28, 30, 87 *foot.*
Henry, Prof. Joseph, acoustical experiments, 122, 126-127, 263, 266
appearance, 28, 32, 65, 73, 74
apprenticed to John Doty, 34
approves Stevens battery, 153, 157, 177-178
and Bache plot to discredit Maury, 137
born Albany, New York, 27
can't find place in world, 63-64
and Centennial Exposition, 267
children, 72, 75, 76, 83, 126, 143, 154, 180, 181, 182, 183, 209, 216, 219-220, 225, 264, 267
Civil War work, lesser, 152, 153, 215-216, 226, 227
Congressional investigation of Smithsonian funds, 123, 124
"the Club," 209
decides to get education, 38-39
Director of the Mint, a, 215
discovers theory of magneto-electricity, 4, 70-72
Early's Raid, 223-225
encourages young scientists, 264-265
European trip, first, 76-78

New Theoretical Practical Treatise on Navigation, 50, 60, 62 *foot.*, 97
New York, 42, 256, 282
New York State, 34, 52
Newcomb, Simon, 159, 168, 184 *foot.*, 170, 225, 260, 266, 268
Niter, 4, 171, 172
Norfolk Navy Yard. *See* Gosport Navy Yard.
North, the, 47, 66, 133, 138, 142, 218
North Atlantic Wind and Current Chart, 103
Nukahiva Island, Marquesas Group, 18-19, 20, 46, 138, 284

Observatory, Lick, 267-268
Observatory, Mexican National, 273
Observatory, United States Naval, 3, 7-8, 95, 97, 98, 100, 101, 103, 106, 110, 111, 112 *foot.*, 129, 133, 135, 137, 159, 168, 169, 170, 255, 260, 282, 284
Oceanography (*see also* Wind and Current Charts, *The Physical Geography of the Sea*, and Maury, Cmdr. Matthew Fontaine), 4, 282
Origin of Species, 138, 139
Orographic map, 108
Owens, Robert Dale, 115

Packet Row, 42
Packet ships, 90, 91, 92
Patterson, Hannah, 129, 183, 217
Paulding, James K., 52, 58, 138
Percival, Capt. John ("Mad Jack"), 59, 101
Permanent Commission, 215, 221

Petersburg, seige of, 227, 241, 255
Phelps, Israel, 30, 31, 32
Physical Geography of the Sea, The, 9, 106, 107, 108, 109, 135, 140, 233
Pierce, Franklin, 4, 110
Pilgrims Progress, 49
Pilot Charts, 103
Poinsett, Joel R., 53
Polk, James K., 21, 98
Port Mahón, Minorca, 43, 61-62 *foot.*, 64
Porter, Capt. David ("Logan"), 20, 21, 49
Potomac River, 3, 7, 100, 177, 258
Potomac, U.S.S., 48
President's House. *See* White House.
Princeton University (College of New Jersey at Princeton), 72, 73, 74, 75, 78, 79, 80, 83, 261
Princeton, U.S.S., 96

Rappahannock, C.S.S., 239, 241-242
Rappahannock River, 12, 218
Redfield, William, 120
Relief, U.S.S., 51, 52
Renwick, James, 52, 114, 115
Retiring Board, U. S. Naval, 110, 125, 133, 134, 135, 142, 246, 287
Revolutionary War, 12, 19, 31
Rhees, William J., 129, 228, 249, 250
Richmond, Virginia, 178, 180, 189-190, 196, 200-201, 255, 282-283, 288
Richmond *Whig,* 53, 54, 58, 277
Rodgers, Commo. John, 43
Rostrum, the, 37, 39